GRENZMANN / DICHTUNG UND GLAUBE

My Weekly

2020 ANNUAL

PAGE
20

PAGE
42

PAGE
96

FICTION

CELEBRITY

FANCY THAT

NO-BAKE TREATS

BRAINBOOSTERS

DC THOMSON MEDIA

Daytime Smiles!

We chat with Holly Willoughby, queen of daytime TV, *This Morning* presenter, and proud mother of three

Favourite Guests

"My favourite celebrity guests are amazing strong women like Joan Collins or Joanna Lumley, but I don't think I could choose a favourite from the incredible human interest stories we get. I do get emotional because I'm really feeling for what they've been through or have overcome. Like the viewers watching, we're often hearing these stories for the first time too, and emotions can take you by surprise."

Joanna Lumley was a favourite guest

Joan Collins

"I Want To Be My Cat!"

It's a cat's life

"If I could swap jobs with anyone for a day it would be my cat – even though she doesn't have a job! But she gets to sleep all day. When I leave in the morning, she's asleep and when I return she's in the same position. If I could do anything for a day, that's what I'd want to do!"

On Being A Mum

"My son, Harry, is massively into football, so I think he's going to be super sporty. Belle's imagination is amazing – she disappears in her own little world and loves writing stories – so maybe something creative. And Chester is a little too small still. But I hope I've armed them with all the tools and knowledge they need to go out and make their own mistakes and learn their own lessons." ➤

Phil Schofield

"I thrive on stuff going pear-shaped or plans going out of the window! I like when it's a little 'whoa, what's going on here?', so TV doesn't make me nervous. It's like a beam of focus. Sometimes your focus is at a normal level and that's your usual presenting style and other times it changes a gear and you think, 'Right, now we have to really centre ourselves here' to cope with whatever it is."

This Morning, weekdays, 10.30am on ITV

Lots Of Laughs

This Morning presenters tell us why they love the show so much – like it's being part of a family!

Ruth Langsford

"I've been doing *This Morning* a very long time now but I still get that thrill! I love coming in and never quite knowing what I'm going to find. Items and running orders can change overnight so you have to be aware of what's going on in the world and showbiz news because you don't know what they're going to throw at you in the morning. But I love that!"

Dr Ranj

"What people don't always realise is the positive impact *This Morning* has had on people. The first aid stuff that we've done actually led to a rise in first aid training in schools. There are so many awareness campaigns, and all the anti-bullying items we do. It just makes me so proud, and that's what makes it more than just a TV show. It's more than that."

Alison Hammond

"There are a lot of reasons I love working on the show! You have an amazing agony aunty at your disposal in the form of Deirdre, you have a fashion guru in the shape of Gok, fantastic Bryony to sort out your makeup, doctors like Chris, Zoe and Ranj are there when you're not well, and chefs like Phil Vickery and Gino who rustle up fantastic food... I mean it's the best TV community ever!" ➜

Great TV

Our daytime TV favourites reveal what they love most about the shows they present...

Loose Women, Coleen Nolan

"I hope I'm always a regular on *Loose Women*. I absolutely love it. I call it my proper job now. I have such a good time. It's a really lovely part of what I do. When I step away from it to do other things and then I go back it's just comforting. It's like going home. Just sitting down and chatting with my girlfriends about what I've been doing."

Countdown, Susie Dent

"I'm privileged to have a job I love. I still feel a surge of adrenaline the moment the clock starts to tick down. Every presenter has been a worthy successor to the meister that was Richard Whiteley. From Des Lynam's twinkly eye and Carol Vorderman's infectious laughter, to Rachel Riley's mind-bending maths and giggling and Nick's mischief. They've all been great!"

Homes Under The Hammer, Martel Maxwell

"I love meeting the contributors. It can be sad, it can be inspiring. Somebody might have died and they want to use the inheritance money to make that person proud. It might be somebody who's tuned in for 14 years and suddenly thought 'I can do that'. I love that! Also, Dion is funny and charming, Martin has been good fun and we have a laugh!"

The Chase, Bradley Walsh

"As long as they continue to ask me, I'll continue to make it! I just love working this job – it doesn't feel like work. It's not a proper job really. And as long as it feels like that, I'll continue to do it. When I'm doing any job, I give it 100% – it gets my absolute focus. But as I approach the prime of my life, I find I'm having the time of my life!"

WORDS: HANNAH MCLAREN PICTURES: ITV PICTURES, PLANET PHOTOS

Adele Parks

City Of Dreams

Katie was determined that the proposal, when it happened, was going to be absolutely perfect...

It wasn't entirely Katie's fault that she had such specific expectations about the trip to Venice. Everyone agreed that a proposal was more-than-likely imminent.

"Everyone" being her mum, her sister and her four closest friends (two married, one single, one "a confirmed bachelor" – as her nan euphemistically called Giles, her friend who was gay). This was a reasonable consensus, a vote of confidence, practically an endorsement of a foregone conclusion, at least as far as Katie was concerned.

She and Harry had been together

for four years and they lived together – admittedly in his flat with his name on the mortgage and utility bills, but Katie bought the groceries and she'd redecorated the place from top to bottom. Her clothes were squashed into the wardrobes and bottom drawers. That meant something. To her, it meant everything.

They travelled club class. An unnecessary luxury for a short haul flight and, Katie thought, proof positive that Harry wanted this to be a particularly special weekend. Her preference was that he'd pop the question promptly, at the beginning.

It was a funny expression, "pop the question". She was the one ready to pop. Burst. Explode with excitement. Perhaps he would do it tonight? Then they could utilise the rest of the time planning the wedding or,

more accurately, Katie telling Harry what she wanted for her big day.

She'd selected the church, venue, menu, band and bridesmaids. She had a good idea about the style of dress too (but all the wedding magazines agreed you didn't really know until you actually tried it on, which dress would be perfect). So, finalising that detail would have to wait.

Harry wasn't generally into big romantic gestures. Which man was? Katie accepted there was a reasonable chance he'd mess it up, propose somewhere unsuitable, like on the plane or in a restaurant. Katie had never liked the idea of restaurant proposals. A few of her friends' boyfriends had gone down that route and the girls always claimed to be happy, but Katie knew she'd be put off her food and she didn't like waste.

Besides, how do you hug and kiss with a table in between and everyone watching?

She wanted to float on a cloud of delicious scent

Same problem on a plane – plus she'd be distracted by that low-grade but ever-present sense of unease that she felt when flying, and the funny smell. Planes always had a funny smell. Katie had a very strong sense of smell so no, that wouldn't do.

She wanted to float on a cloud of the scent of baked bread, freshly cut grass or heady, full lilies when she was proposed to. Although she hadn't worked out exactly which scent was most likely to be the backdrop in Venice. The freshly cut grass was perhaps a stretch.

Katie talked non-stop on the plane so Harry wouldn't find opportunity to ask. She chattered about the funny plastic cutlery, her ankles swelling on flights, ➜

whether it was worth sending postcards, did anyone still do that? Anything, rather than him ruin her big moment by proposing somewhere inappropriate.

They emerged from the airport and Katie was thrilled to see a beautiful mahogany boat waiting to take them to the mainland. As they slipped through the sea, the late autumn sun made everything appear glittery, the breeze lifted Katie's hair and she felt like a Bond girl. Now, the boat limousine, would have been an ideal place to propose, she thought.

"Isn't this just perfect?" she said, staring intently at Harry.

"Bit blowy," he replied, without taking his eyes off the map he was scouring.

Harry had an innate distrust of taxi drivers and always made a big deal of following their chosen route on a map. Whether that be from pub to home or airport to hotel, he was keen to ensure the cabbie took the most direct path.

Katie doubted he had any idea how to read a map of waterways, so she sank back into the leather seat and tried to ignore her sense of an opportunity missed.

number of photo-worthy proposal spots in that plan. She fully intended to capture the moment digitally and post it on at least five social media channels.

She wasn't usually bothered about social media. The whole thing struck her as artificial and a little showy-offie; normally she preferred to enjoy the moment, rather than offer it up for casual Likes. It was something she and Harry agreed on, but her proposal was a different beast. Of course, she would need to take loads of photos – and besides the perfect backdrop she would absolutely have to look the part.

So she insisted on taking a quick shower and changing her outfit. It wouldn't do to be proposed to in the jeans she'd travelled in.

In the end, it took about an hour and a half for Katie to shower, exfoliate, reapply make-up and select the outfit she did want to be wearing when she agreed to become Mrs Johnson. Unfortunately, by that time, the sun had slipped away for the night. It was a bit cloudy and damp.

Katie was determined to ignore the fact, just as she tried to ignore Harry's grumbles

She'd imagined herself in new va-va-voom shoes that made her calves taut

It was almost three o'clock by the time they dropped off their bags at the hotel. Harry suggested they went straight out to make the most of the late afternoon sunshine that was casting long shadows, clothing the streets in a glamour that wasn't available in the wet, soggy autumnal street at home. He suggested that perhaps they could buy an ice cream, stretch their legs. Or if it was too late in the season to reasonably consider afternoon ice creams, then maybe a dark, treacly espresso in a café in a piazza somewhere.

Katie agreed, instantly envisaging a

and specifically his comment that stilettos were impractical in the cobbled streets. "What's wrong with your comfy trainers?"

Katie was in love with Venice. She had decided it was the most romantic place in the world the moment Harry mentioned he'd booked a mini-break. She'd read all about the Doges' Palace and had imagined them strolling through Piazza San Marco and taking a trip to the Accademia for weeks now. She had imagined she'd do so in brand new va-va-voom shoes that made her calves look taut; true, she'd not factored in how many steps and cobbles she would have to negotiate – but comfy trainers and a proposal? That would never do!

Venice did not stink. Katie had never believed it would, despite all the grim warnings she'd had from people like the woman in the dry cleaners, Dave from next door and the lads in the post-room at her office – people who didn't have an ounce of romance in their bodies. True, there was a something lingering in the air but that was the same with all towns and cities that nudged up against water. It was atmospheric. Katie reached inside her bag and pulled out her perfume bottle. She squirted it generously all over her neck, wrists and clothes. To be on the safe side she surreptitiously squirted a bit on Harry too. He glowered and coughed.

"What are you doing?"

"Nothing – nothing at all."

They mooched around the baroque backstreets, stood outside churches and wandered across umpteen pretty bridges. Despite the lines of washing flapping in the breeze Katie thought these streets had a shabby charm and were perfect backdrops to popping the question.

Clearly, Harry did not agree. He kept resolutely silent despite her numerous hints about how romantic everything was and how perfect. They ambled along the waters of St Mark's Basin. How was it described in the guide book? *A mirror to reflect the majesty and splendour of the Basilica of San Giorgio Maggiore.* A perfect place for a proposal.

Katie dawdled. She leaned her elbows on the iron railing of a bridge and gazed out onto the canals as though enchanted. It was a lovely view, though she hadn't expected the temperatures to drop quite so dramatically. In her imaginings they were always walking in the sunshine. People had mentioned that it could get chilly in

November but she had countered, "It's Italy, I've been before. I know what to expect."

"You've only been once, to the south, in August," pointed out her mum. Katie wasn't certain, but she thought her mum might have rolled her eyes. She wished now she had taken the advice and packed a heavier jacket, perhaps a jumper.

Harry leaned his bum against the railings and looked in the opposite direction. Katie tried not to be disconcerted.

"Harry, isn't this just so wonderful?" she asked as she gently bit her lower lip.

Last week they'd been watching Graham Norton on TV. They'd devoured a takeaway and polished off the best part of a bottle of wine. They'd chomped their way through half a box of Roses – not the type of confectionery Katie would ever take to a dinner party, but their favourite. Graham Norton was interviewing Hollywood's latest hot actress; she had repeatedly bitten her lower lip in a very provocative way. Harry had been mesmerised.

"Do you have a mouth ulcer, love?" he asked Katie now.

"No, why?"

"You keep chewing your lip. I thought you were in pain. I've got some Bonjela in my wash bag. I'll dig it out for you."

"I don't have a mouth ulcer."

"Maybe you've started to bite your lip as a compensation for giving up biting your nails," he suggested.

She had always been a nail biter; Harry hated the habit and had often urged her to stop. She had tried to, on countless occasions but had never gone longer than two days without caving in and having a nibble. That was until she imagined something sparkly on her third finger, left hand. Stumpy nails would so ruin the effect.

"No," she mumbled, somewhat exasperated. Clearly, her provocative lower lip nibbling was doing nothing for Harry. She looked around for something to talk ➜

about but despite the wealth of history, culture and bars she was stumped.

They endured a ten-minute silence, the first of their relationship.

Eventually Harry asked, "Do you fancy something to eat? The local dish of squid pasta is supposed to be worth trying –"

"I'm tired, let's just go back to the hotel. To bed." And so that he was absolutely clear, she added sternly, "To sleep."

Saturday followed the same pattern. Katie woke up hopeful and dressed in a way she thought appropriate for accepting a proposal. Harry woke up bewildered and a little resentful that a romantic mini-break in Venice hadn't culminated in even a whiff of sex. Despite the top-notch hotel with four-poster bed.

but what was normal about your girlfriend holding a gun to your head, full of emotional bullets that she so clearly wanted to spend?

He'd planned to take her to Santa Maria Gloriosa dei Frari, arguably one of Venice's most sublime religious treasure troves, to see Titian's gloriously uplifting *Assumption* altar painting. He'd wanted to propose to her in front of that painting; he was also capable of assuming, planning and plotting. But her needy expectations had ruined everything. He felt she was presuming, second-guessing and worst of all, *waiting*. Now he felt that he might return to England with the Princess cut diamond still snugly tucked up in his jacket pocket.

By Sunday they were barely speaking. Katie insisted she didn't want to go to a market (unheard of); Harry said he had no appetite for restaurants (a first). Instead of enjoying the cafe orchestras, cooing pigeons

It seemed the crowds were made up entirely of besotted lovers

His bewilderment and resentment grew as Katie spent the day acting increasingly oddly. Normally so relaxed and such a laugh, she'd started to behave in a way that defied belief. Did she think he was a complete moron? He wasn't impervious to her lingering near particularly picturesque backdrops and outside jewellers' windows.

He knew what she wanted, but frankly her behaviour was terrifying.

He had been going to do it. Of course he had. Why not? The woman was a marvel; he adored her. Or at least he thought he adored her. But her peculiar, pushy behaviour was making him... nervous.

Suddenly, he didn't like the way she munched her food and her walk was funny, sort of lopsided. This wouldn't have been a deal-breaker under normal circumstances,

and waiters serving alfresco diners, Katie complained that St Mark's Square was too boisterous. She rushed towards a gondola, no longer envisaging romantic opportunities (she'd given up on that – it was Sunday evening, they were leaving early next day) but she desperately wanted to be away from the crowds, which as far as she could see were entirely made up of besotted lovers.

These besotted lovers didn't mean to mock and taunt her, but they did. Their eye-gazing, hand-holding, and stealing of secret kisses highlighted the fact she and Harry were behaving like strangers.

She felt her insides being gnawed by bitter disappointment and humiliation. She didn't know how much longer she could hold back her tears or her temper. She feared that one thing, or the other, was about to surge out of her. She was ready to pop but no longer with giddy excitement.

They gently drifted on a gondola, moving away from the crowds. Katie lay back and stared at the stars glistening in the navy sky. She wondered if she could be bothered to comment to Harry that the scene was perfect. No doubt he'd ask, "Perfect for what?" in an impatient voice, as he had every other time she'd helpfully pointed out the perfect moments on their trip. Not that there had been so many today.

Of course, everything was still as interesting, steeped in history, culturally amazing as when they'd first arrived. Only somehow things were far from perfect now.

Harry asked the gondolier to stop singing. He was barely polite about it, and usually he had such great manners.

"What's up?" asked Katie, although she wasn't sure she wanted to know. She was terrified as to where a conversation starting that way might lead.

"I have a headache," Harry replied.

Katie had never known him to suffer from headaches before. He started to mutter something about the whole experience being excruciating and a rip-off to boot.

She knew that the cost of hiring a gondolier was eye-watering. Only really worth it if the experience was one which would be recalled for years to come. That scenario seemed unlikely.

She supposed she would have to finish it. Them. This. They were not going to have years ahead of them, looking back. She couldn't just sit around forever and wait for Harry to finally decide she was the woman for him – or worse, decide she wasn't.

But she loved him so.

She couldn't imagine life without him. It sounded dramatic, but it was true. They were great together. Usually. Other people often commented on it. Spontaneously, they'd laugh and say things like, "Oh, you guys are adorable together."

Katie wondered what to do next. It was all so depressing and wrong. Nothing was turning out as she'd hoped and now she found she could indeed detect unsavoury wafts of something pungent from the sewer and stale sweat from the gondolier's T-shirt.

Harry felt miserable. He had thought the break would be such a laugh. He had really splashed out; good flights, cool hotel, booked the best restaurants. Not that they had honoured a booking as yet.

He wondered if the jewellers accepted returns. What a waste. Not just of money but other stuff, bigger stuff. He'd really thought she was his soulmate. The One.

Things couldn't get any worse – unless of course he lost the ring… Panic! Harry self-frisked in a frantic attempt to locate it.

"What is it?" asked Katie.

"The ring! I've lost it. On top of you being a freak I've lost the damned ring."

"What?"

"Sorry, I didn't mean to call you a freak."

"I meant the other bit. What ring?"

"An engagement ring, of course," he snapped. Snapped, a little like popped. "It's so dark. I can't believe this! Will you?"

"Yes. I will."

"Look for it!"

"Oh, right. I thought you meant –"

"I'm unlikely to propose the moment I've lost the ring, am I?"

Katie was already on her hands and knees. She'd forgotten she was wearing high heels and white jeans. She groped around the damp, dark gondola floor. Her bottom bobbed up and down inelegantly and something shifted back into place for Harry. Katie no longer seemed overly keen or controlling. She was concerned and well-meaning again. His gut turned.

"I'll do you a deal. If we do find the ring, I will propose. OK?"

"Deal – and if I like the ring I'll accept," she replied with a grin. Ⓜ

Turn over to find out more about best-selling author Adele Parks

Road To Success

Adele was on the fast track to fame with her very first novel, and values her readers' views most of all…

The first time I had anything in print was a poem in a magazine called *Blue Jeans* when I was about 14 years old. It was about heartbreak, even though I had never had my heart broken at that stage in my life. When I saw it in print, I was a little embarrassed by it, because I felt exposed, but also thrilled. Writing is exposing if it's raw and emotional.

Hoping to get my debut novel published, I sent an unsolicited manuscript to an agent at Curtis Brown Literary Agency. I went away for the weekend to celebrate my birthday and when I returned there was a message on my answering machine saying he liked my work and was interested in meeting me to discuss it. I cried with happiness and listened to that message about a hundred times.

When I had re-drafted my manuscript a number of times, my agent sent the novel, which was called *Playing Away*, out to a number of publishers. Within days there was a bidding war between six publishing houses. Subsequently I was able to quit my day job and become a full-time writer. *Playing Away* also sold in Germany and the USA within a week or two. It was an utterly amazing time.

Funnily enough it's not the big award ceremonies that make me feel my writing is important, it's when I get letters from readers. They'll take great pains to tell me why my books move them, what they relate to, what is going on in their world. It's very humbling to know my words have some power to console, entertain or inspire when people are going through tough patches.

I have published 18 novels in as many years. I'm thrilled to say they have all been bestsellers and launch time is always exciting. Although I never quite get used to seeing my books in the charts and I certainly don't take it for granted. Last year, my novel *I Invited Her In* was in the top of the charts for many weeks, hitting the number 2 spot! I'm keeping my fingers crossed that my next novel *Lies, Lies, Lies* might even beat that! Ⓜ

Adele's latest novel *Lies, Lies, Lies* is published September 2019, HQ £7.99

FANCY THAT!

Fascinating facts on **Chocolate!**

✦ **The biggest chocolate bar in the world was created in the UK in 2011. It weighed 5.7 tons!**

✦ The blood in the famous shower scene of the movie *Psycho* was in fact chocolate syrup.

✦ It takes almost a full year for a cocoa tree to produce enough pods to make 10 standard-sized chocolate bars.

✦ **Winston Churchill loved chocolate so much that at one point the Nazis plotted to assassinate him with an exploding bar of chocolate!**

✦ **Chocolate has over 600 flavour compounds, while red wine has only 200.**

✦ The word chocolate comes from the Aztec word "xocolatl" which means "bitter water".

✦ **The scientific name for the tree from which chocolate comes is Theobroma cacao, which means "food of the gods".**

✦ Chocolate now comes in a new colour – pink! Ruby chocolate is a natural discovery by a Swiss company that found the new species of cocoa bean that produces a pink powder.

✦ Just the smell of chocolate increases theta brain waves, thus triggering relaxation.

✦ **Dark chocolate with more than 50% cocoa solids contains antioxidants that are effective against ageing, cancer, high blood pressure, heart disease, and improves your immune system.**

✦ White chocolate is not actually chocolate as it does not contain cocoa solids, only cocoa butter.

✦ **The Mayans believed chocolate was a gift from the gods, and even used it as currency.**

✦ The inventor of the chocolate chip cookie sold his idea to Nestlé in exchange for a lifetime supply of chocolate!

Chocolate increases levels of our "happy hormones", endorphin and dopamine

Family Christmas?

When Anna's mother-in-law steps through the door into frazzled chaos, things surely can't end well…

By Hazel E. Kendrick

T he area around the school was chaotic and Anna was late. Parking spaces were rare at the best of times, and this was the last day of term before Christmas, with sleety rain deluging from a darkening sky.

Luckily, a car moved out from the crowded kerbside and Anna edged into its space. She did not normally bring the car to meet Matthew, but the weather was so awful they would have been soaked in moments walking home.

Anna put up the hood of her weatherproof coat and climbed out. Children were streaming past now, the freezing air filled with their excited laughter. Car doors slammed, the crowd of children lessened. Anna thought of the tasks still waiting to be done before Harry came back, bringing his mother to stay for the holidays. At the thought of Harry's mother, Anna's insides tightened with apprehension.

Matthew finally appeared, walking ➤

oddly, almost on tiptoe. Behind came his teacher, Mrs Clarke. Mrs Clarke was carrying a mysterious covered square object. Anna hastened to meet them.

Mrs Clarke beamed at her.

"Ah! Mrs Deacon. Here we are. So kind of you to agree to this."

Mrs Clarke held the mysterious square object towards Anna, who automatically reached for it.

"Matthew has everything else in his bag." Mrs Clarke turned away. "Goodbye, then. Have a really lovely Christmas."

Somebody was beeping impatiently close by and Anna realised she had parked too far from the kerb. Hastily, she got Matthew and the object into the car and headed for home.

"My feet hurt," Matthew declared plaintively. "My boots don't fit!"

Anna sighed. "Of course they fit, Matthew. We only bought them last week,

"Who is Daisy?" Anna demanded as soon as they got in. She eyed the covered box with sudden apprehension.

"She's our hamster," Matthew said happily. "She lives in the classroom, but she needs looking after till we go back and you said we could do it, Mummy." He patted his school bag, "I've got all her food and water bottle."

Anna felt as though the icy chill had followed them into the house. A hamster! With Harry's mother due here very soon, who had a positive rodent phobia. Was a hamster actually a rodent?

And speaking of rodents – what about Sylvester? Sylvester, their handsome green-eyed black cat from whom no butterfly, spider or field mouse was safe.

"Take Daisy straight up to your room, Matthew," Anna said firmly. "I'll distract Sylvester with a sardine. Take off those wet boots then just go! Shut your

Matthew, scarlet-faced, tugged at his boots which appeared to be glued on

remember? And I don't recall agreeing to anything! What's in that box?"

In her mirror Anna could dimly see that Matthew was beaming.

"Daisy, of course! You were on the phone, Mummy, and I showed you my letter that Mrs Clarke wanted signed? And you signed it while you were still talking."

The scene slid into Anna's reluctant mind. Yes, she'd been talking to a plumber about a dripping tap in the bathroom. Trying to sort out if it could be fixed as soon as possible because they were on a water meter – but just what was it that she had signed for?

It was still deluging down, but at least they were now home. Anna backed onto the driveway, leaving room for Harry's returning car.

bedroom door when you come out!"

Sylvester was delighted with the surprise of a sardine in the afternoon, but after polishing his saucer clean, went to the kitchen door and set up a constant miaowing.

Pushing him away, slipping through and then hastily closing the door, Anna returned to the hall. Matthew still sat on the bottom stair, scarlet-faced, tugging at his boots which appeared to be glued on. Beside him, Daisy's home remained covered and very quiet.

"Why can't you get your boots off, Matthew?" Anna demanded. "Have you put them on the wrong feet?" She knelt on the hall floor and joined in the tugging. Eventually both boots, with Matthew's socks still inside them, came off.

Anna picked one up with a frown. Odd. She had written her son's name in marker pen inside each boot only days ago. Now there was nothing written at all.

"My feet hurt!" Matthew said plaintively. "I said my new boots didn't fit me!"

They were not new boots, Anna realised. They were quite old boots and a size one, whereas Matthew was a two and a half. They'd bought a size three to allow for thick socks and rapid growth.

Anna sat back on her heels.

"Matthew, these are not your new boots. They're somebody else's old ones. Where are yours, with your name in?"

But Matthew had lost interest in the boots. He was carefully lifting a corner of Daisy's cover to see if she'd woken up.

There was only one explanation, Anna thought suddenly. Another child, who owned these boots, had gone home in Matthew's new ones before Matthew had got to the cloakroom with Mrs Clarke and Daisy – and it was the last day of term, so there was no chance of sorting things out until January.

Mentally, Anna added *new wellies* to her lengthening list of things still to get done. They would be a short-term stopgap.

Suddenly there was the slam of a car door outside and the sound of Harry's cheerful voice.

"Sit there a moment, Mum," the voice said. "I'll come round and help you. That sleet is turning to ice now. The temperature's dropping again. Wouldn't be surprised if we got snow!"

"It's Daddy and Grandma!" Matthew squealed in delight. He jumped from the stairs in his bare feet, catching the edge of Daisy's covered cage as he did so. As though in slow motion Anna watched in disbelief as the cage overbalanced, fell, and somehow knocked the cage door wide open against the hall table.

From the cage emerged a small, golden creature that immediately scuttled out of sight through the open living-room door.

"No! No! Come back!" Matthew cried out, racing after it.

Anna just had time to whip up the cage and hide it under Matthew's discarded coat before the front door opened and Harry entered, accompanied by his mother.

Rose Deacon was an imposing woman. Tall and elegant, dressed today in a royal blue coat and matching hat which sat at a jaunty angle on her silver hair. Anna had never seen Rose look anything but immaculate. She ran her life like a military operation, was president of her local WI and terrified Anna to bits.

Matthew raced back into the hall.

"Grandma!"

Rose folded her arms about Matthew in a graceful hug.

"Hello, darling. Goodness, your bare ➡

toes must be icy cold! Where are your slippers?"

Where indeed? Anna thought glumly.

Matthew remembered Daisy and his expression changed to sorrow. "Grandma! I've lost…"

"His boots!" Anna interjected hurriedly. "Someone went home in Matthew's new ones and he had to come home in theirs."

Rose ruffled Matthew's hair.

"Well now. Never mind. I'll get you some more tomorrow. We'll put your name in them this time! Harry dear, would you carry my case up to my bedroom?"

Anna gritted her teeth as Rose moved away like royalty. Harry followed, struggling with a large suitcase. He raised his eyebrows at Anna as he passed.

"All OK?" he whispered, grinning as Rose vanished on to the landing.

"Fine!" she hissed back. "But keep your mother upstairs as long as you can. Show her something. Anything!"

Harry's grin vanished. "What?"

"Just do it, Harry!"

The living room was strewn with a muddle of things Anna had meant to sort out before going to pick up Matthew. Matthew himself sat in the middle of them, fat tears dripping down his face.

"I can't find her!" he sobbed. He looked helplessly around him. "Daisy? Daisy?"

Give me your answer do, Anna thought hysterically. She pulled Matthew into her arms and stroked his hair.

"Ssh. We'll find her, but best not to tell Grandma about Daisy just yet. We'll put some of Daisy's food down and put her cage nearby with some more."

After this was accomplished, Anna persuaded Matthew to leave the room and they shut the door firmly behind them. Surely Daisy would want to get back to her own home, wouldn't she?

With this thought in mind Anna returned to the kitchen, instructing Matthew to find clean socks and his

slippers, and then to go and show Grandma the model fire engine he'd made from the kit she'd sent for his birthday.

Two things greeted Anna in the kitchen. The first, of course, was Sylvester. A Sylvester fully alert, tail waving, nose sniffing like a bloodhound.

Sylvester's one desire was to get out of the kitchen and set off on a tour of exploration throughout the house. *Something smells different,* his curious feline face seemed to say and he, Sylvester, intended to find out what it was.

Thwarted by this desire by Anna, he set up a mournful howl that was only quelled by another sardine.

The second thing to greet Anna was the aroma, or rather the lack of one. By now, surely the scent of a good, rich beef casserole should be wafting from the slow cooker on the worktop? Or it would have been… had Anna remembered to switch it on hours ago.

Anna resisted the desire to scream and frantically searched the fridge and cupboards for a quick alternative. Plenty of pasta. Anna could make tomato sauce for it – although hadn't Rose said once that pasta gave her indigestion? There was a pack of cook-from-frozen chicken in the freezer. Maybe…?

Anna's thoughts were interrupted by the entrance of Harry. Luckily, alone, as she could hear Rose's voice still upstairs talking to Matthew about his model.

"OK. Explain!" Harry said sternly. "What's up?"

Anna took a deep breath and told him. They returned to the living-room together where Harry immediately set about

Claus. To Anna's relief, the footsteps moved on towards the kitchen.

Her relief was short-lived as a moment later, a long pitiful miaow sounded from the outside of the living-room door. They had let Sylvester out!

"May we come in?" said Rose's well-modulated voice from outside the door. "Or are there secrets going on?"

"Can't hide anything from you, Mum, can we?" Harry called with false jollity, "but we won't be long now!"

"There's a Christmas secret, all right," Anna muttered. "Small and a bit mouse-like!" She raised her voice. "Rose, can you possibly give Sylvester a packet of cat food, please? Matthew, you can show Grandma where they are."

There were murmurs of assent and the sound of footsteps fading away.

"Why don't we just let Sylvester in and let him find the thing?" Harry suggested

"No!" Anna and Harry yelled in panicked unison. There was a surprised pause

searching every corner with the torch he'd brought with him.

"Nothing!" he said at last, sitting back on his heels. "Why on earth did you agree to taking the hamster, Anna? You know Mum is…"

There was a sudden scuttling nearby and a quick glimpse of a small golden animal vanishing again behind the sofa. Anna and Harry lunged at it, banging their heads together as they did so. They glared at one another, each rubbing their noses.

"If you had rung the plumber, I'd never have agreed to it!" Anna said crossly.

"Rung the…? What are you on about?"

Anna was spared from replying by the sound of two sets of footsteps coming down the stairs and Matthew's eager voice talking to Harry's mum about Santa

tiredly. "I think you've broken my nose! Is it bleeding?"

"No, but it will be if you make any more suggestions like that!"

"Well, we can't stay in here all evening. What's for supper?"

"I've absolutely no idea!"

They both jumped as Rose's voice came again from outside the door.

"Anna? Matthew was hungry, so I've done him beans on toast. Hope that's OK – and I've made us a cup of tea. Do you want it in there?"

"No!" Anna and Harry yelled in panicked unison.

There was a surprised pause.

"Oh, well, it's all ready in the kitchen when you are, then. I brought some of my butterfly cakes." ➡

Harry got to his feet decisively.

"This is useless, Anna. I'm just going to have to tell Mum what's happened. I'm not missing out on her butterfly cakes!" He opened the door carefully, inched out and closed it behind him.

The traitor! Anna thought, tears stinging her eyes, unable to even begin to imagine how Rose would react. Maybe she would demand that Harry make the drive back immediately to take her home? Christmas would be ruined! Matthew would be in tears for hours and Sylvester? Maybe he really would be the one to find Daisy. How would she explain that to Matthew's teacher in January?

time Jane came back, I rather liked that man and he seemed to like me, too. I've been on my own a long time, Anna. It's rather nice to be going out with someone and Pearl is awfully sweet."

"His daughter?" Anna asked faintly.

"No, Pearl is his favourite hamster. He breeds them. That's why he was at the vet's that day. Pearl was pregnant. Her babies are adorable." Rose got to her feet. "Michael, his name is… the man I mean. You'd like him, Anna. I know you would. I hope Harry will, too."

There was a new softness about Rose that was really nice.

Still somewhat stunned at Rose's

"Shall we send out for pizza? The casserole will be nicely marinated for tomorrow"

The door opened and closed again and the room became scented with Rose's perfume. To Anna's surprise, Rose sat down beside her on the floor and put a comforting arm around her shoulders.

"Let me help!" she said softly.

It was another hour and a half before Daisy was found, fast asleep under the Christmas tree. Rose picked her up gently and returned her to her cage.

"What a poppet!" she said fondly.

Anna stared.

"You've always hated rodents!"

"Only the verminous ones. Rats and suchlike. I've come to quite like the small domestic ones."

Rose looked at Anna with a sudden smile that lit up her face.

"I've met someone, Anna. Quite by chance. My friend Jane asked if I'd drive her to the vet's. Her dog was poorly. After she went in, I got talking to this man in the waiting room.

"The vet was running late and by the

revelations, Anna remembered supper, or rather the lack of one, and confessed. To Anna's relief, Rose laughed.

"Don't worry. I expect you've been rushing around doing a hundred things at once. I remember Christmases when Harry and his sister were small. Hectic wasn't the word!

"Now, what do you say if we send out for a pizza? I'm sure Harry would like that, too and the beef casserole will be nicely marinated for tomorrow."

Rose held out a hand to Anna to help her up. Almost as though she knew about the new baby – but it was very early days, so only Harry knew about that. Maybe, Anna thought, it wouldn't be such a bad Christmas after all. MW

THE FIRST BOOK I READ…

Ballet Shoes about three little girls who went on the stage. A prize when I was 11. Still have that much-loved book, yellowing and well Sellotaped now!

Brain Boosters

Codeword

Each letter of the alphabet has been replaced by a number. The numbers for the first name of our chosen celebrity are given. Complete the puzzle to find out where *Great British Bake Off* presenter Sandi Toksvig completed her higher education, and began her comedy career.

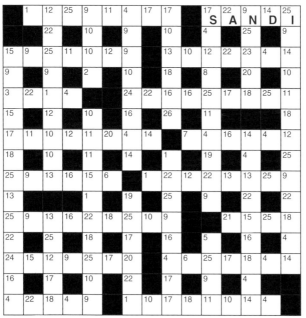

A̶ B C D̶ E F G H I̶ J K L M N̶ O P Q R S̶ T U V W X Y Z

1	2	3	4	5	6	7	8	9 N	10	11	12	13
14 D	15	16	17 S	18	19	20	21	22 A	23	24	25 I	26

Turn To Page 165 For Solutions

23	25 I	12	18	10	9 N		11	10	16	16	4	23	4

11 A	22	19	24	12	25	14 I	23 D	4		15	9 N	25 I	8	4	12	17 S	25 I	18	26

The Gift Of Giving

I had won Tim in the charity auction… or, his time to do household chores, but how would I keep him busy?

By S. Bee

C an I help you?' I asked the young, good-looking, jean-clad guy on the doorstep.

I'd assumed he was trying to sell me something, yet he seemed vaguely familiar… there was no ID card slung around his neck and he wasn't carry a clipboard.

"I'm your Afternoon Help", he beamed.

"There must be a misunderstanding. I haven't hired a cleaner." I began to shut the door.

"I'm Tim! You won me at Sally's charity auction – remember?"

smirks, yet at the time, I happened to be struggling with a bit of DIY.

Since my ex-hubby had exited the scene with a former neighbour, the unfamiliar household tasks had fallen to me: wallpapering the living room and re-grouting the bathroom.

Tim's "help duty" had popped up just at the right time. And, as I was the highest bidder, I'd won!

"That was ages ago," I said.

"Sorry. I've been away travelling," he said, as he fluttered his eyelashes!

I remembered that Sally had mentioned it. "You won't be able to use Tim straight away because he's busy

I had actually planned to luxuriate in a long me-time afternoon on the sofa

The charity auction! Of course! But Sally's fund raiser had been held in October. Today was December 15th.

I recalled that some wag had suggested she offer her student nephew up for auction for "Afternoon help" duty – and hunky, single, twenty-five year-old Tim had agreed.

The highest bidder would win him, and from twelve noon to five pm, they could "use him however they liked".

There was a lot of knowing looks and

studying, plus he works part-time. But don't worry, Jackie, I'll send him round on his next half-term holiday."

And now Tim had arrived on my doorstep.

How was I going to keep him busy for an entire afternoon?

Y ou'd better come in." I know I sounded ungracious, but Tim had called on my day off.

I'd planned to luxuriate in a long,

foam-filled bath. After that, I'd settle on the sofa to watch a feel-good Christmas film with an early Christmas treat – a box of Belgian chocs.

Tim glanced at his watch.

"It's precisely twelve noon. You've got me until five. What can I do for you?"

I swept aside the more obvious answer, and racked my brains.

"To be honest Tim, I'm not quite sure. Look, why don't you tell Sally that you've tidied my garden? When Sally rings, I'll confirm it, and –"

He pouted. "That's cheating."

"The charity benefited. That's the most important thing. Don't you need to do any Christmas shopping of your own?"

Would he take the hint? I'd really looked forward to that bath, telly and chocs I'd had planned.

He clapped his hands. "Christmas! We could do some Christmassy things. Have you decorated your tree yet?"

"I haven't bothered with it this year, because it's such a faff, dragging it down from the loft."

"That's my first job. I'll need a set of ladders though."

Luckily, although my rotten rat of an ex had taken most of the furniture, he'd forgotten the ladders.

So Tim eagerly got to work. ➤

We spent the next few hours happily absorbed. Tim even patiently untangled the lights. The rat had left them in a horrid, twisted mess.

The tree, complete with a sparkly gold star, looked lovely in the corner between the sofa and the window.

"There! That's finished. What's next?"

"Er…"

"I know! Let's make some mince pies."

"But I haven't got any of the ingredients," I stuttered.

"I'll nip to the supermarket and get them. Do you need groceries? I may as well pick them up while I'm there."

I hastily wrote out a list, then handed him some cash and a few Bags for Life. He beetled out to his car and set off.

As I was making coffee, the phone rang. It was Sally.

"Has Tim turned up?"

"Yes. He's helped me decorate the Christmas tree."

"Good. What's he doing now?"

"Shopping for groceries," I replied.

That reminded me – I'd need to dig out my mum's old recipe book. I hadn't made mince pies for years.

Tim and I had great fun making the mince pies.

After we'd measured out the flour and marg, we cracked open a bottle of white wine and got a bit giggly.

Yet surprisingly, the pies came out absolutely perfect.

"Take some for you and Sally," I said, as I hunted around for a tupperware box.

"Have you got any presents that need to be wrapped?" he asked.

"No."

"Any cards to write?"

"No."

I glanced at the clock. "It's just past four thirty. There's no need for you to hang about, Tim. You've done enough. Thanks for your help."

Then I heard a key turn in the door and a voice rang out, "Hi, it's me!" Footsteps headed to the kitchen. "I've had a pig of a day. Oh – hello."

My partner halted in his tracks when he discovered a prime piece of male eye candy lounging against my worktop.

In the middle of my explanation, Tim's mobile bleeped. "A text from my girlfriend. I forgot I was meeting her today. I must go. Bye!"

And finally, he left.

"As you spend most of your time at mine, I thought you weren't bothering with your tree," my partner said.

"I had to find him something to do."

James is the former neighbour's ex-hubby. We'd got together when he'd helped me with the DIY.

I'm selling up and moving in with him soon. Well, I mused, the tree would give the place a homely feel – good for potential buyers.

The fresh wallpaper in the living room and the expert fresh grouting in bathroom could also be taken into account.

And the gift of giving continued when I picked up the plate on the counter top and offered it to James.

Fancy a mince pie?" I smiled.

. . . .

THE FIRST BOOK I READ…

The first novels I remember reading were the *Famous Five* series by Enid Blyton. I was around 8 or 9 when, as a regular library user, I eagerly scooped up the next adventure!

RECIPE AND FOOD STYLING: KATHRYN HAWKINS PHOTOGRAPHY: LIGHTHOUSE PHOTOGRAPHY

Fruit And Nut Garlands

Ingredients (Makes 6)

- ◆ 6 x syrup-filled round waffles (Stroopwafels)
- ◆ 15g unsalted butter
- ◆ 80g golden syrup
- ◆ Green food colour gel or paste
- ◆ 100g nutty granola, lightly crushed
- ◆ 25g flaked almonds
- ◆ 75g green or red glacé cherries, chopped
- ◆ 20g piece red ready-to-roll icing
- ◆ Edible silver balls, to decorate

1 Cut out the centre of each waffle using a 3-4cm diameter round cookie cutter or point of a knife, and place on a board lined with baking parchment.

2 Put the butter and syrup in a saucepan and heat gently until melted. Remove from the heat and mix in sufficient green colour to make a bright shade. Mix in the granola, almonds and cherries until well coated.

3 Working on one garland at a time, carefully spoon the granola mix round the edge of each cookie to cover it completely. Leave to cool completely.

4 Just before serving, break up the red icing and form into little balls. Arrange on the garlands along with the silver balls and serve as soon after decorating as possible.

The Best Bridesmaid

Chloe loves ironing out wedding traumas – but will she ever have time to find her own happy-ever-after?

By Cilla Moss

Two days to go...

Great Aunt Louisa's arriving early at the train station – can you meet her and take her to her hotel? I'm still getting my nails done!

Chloe sighed at her phone. This was the third text she'd had from Summer today. Chloe had been a bridesmaid plenty of times and knew the job could be demanding, but this was another level.

Did she even have time to get to the station? It was thirty minutes from the dog trainer, where she'd taken Mojo the terrier for his last training session before the Big Day. Mojo would be carrying the rings.

She'd just have to make time. It was her job; she couldn't complain.

She wouldn't complain – because she loved it.

There was a reason Chloe was asked so often to be a bridesmaid; she was really good at it. She had been chief bridesmaid for her sister, her cousin, and even an old teacher who had got married the week after she retired. It was sometimes a struggle to fit everything in, but she was an organisational genius – if she did say so herself.

To Chloe there was nothing prettier in the world than a stuffed lever arch file with happy little sticky notes fluttering on the edges like confetti.

She arrived at the station with time to spare. "Hello!" she said cheerily to the eighty-something lady with pink-tinted hair and astonishingly muddy boots, who landed on the crowded platform looking both excited and totally helpless. "I'm your driver. Let me take that case for you. I hope you don't mind dogs? Only I've got a very self-important terrier in my back seat…"

One day to go...

Red alert! Change of plans re hair (headpiece catastrophe!) Need stylist's number urgently!

Trust Summer to have lost the hairdresser's number. Chloe found it in her contacts and sent it straight away.

She was delivering table favours to the reception venue – little boxes of chocolate assortments she and Summer had spent hours putting together.

Where are you?? Can you call in at the church to check on the flowers?

The church looked amazing. As Chloe walked up the aisle she met Ian, the florist, adding the final touches. He gave her a welcoming smile across a bunch of peach gerbera and roses and her heart made a leap. Was that for the stunning flowers, or the unexpectedly handsome florist?

"It looks beautiful," she said.

"Thanks! I hope Summer will be pleased with it all."

How could she not be?

Before she could answer, her phone chimed with another text, and Ian grinned. "Pre-wedding panic?"

"How did you guess?"

"Fancy a pause and a cup of tea? I've got a flask with me."

"Oh, I'd love to –"

She was cut off by her phone chiming again.

"…But I can't."

He looked sweetly disappointed.

"Is it all right if I give you my number?" She blushed. "I mean, in case you need me… Summer's rushed off her feet."

Back at her car she tucked away his business card and hoped she might find a reason to use it. Then she checked her email and found a message from Summer, with a document attached.

Would you read my speech? Could do with some fresh eyes!

Wedding Day

As much as Chloe loved being a bridesmaid, her favourite part was at the end of it all when, satisfied with a job well done, she could relax and have a dance with her friends.

Late in the evening she was pleasantly tipsy and doing *The Macarena* when her phone pinged with a new text from Summer. Chloe braced herself, prepared for another request.

It's been a perfect day, Chloe – thanks for a great job!

Chloe melted, forgiving on the spot every bad-tempered, ill-timed message Summer had ever sent.

Something made her look up. Across the dance floor, Summer held up her phone with a cheeky wink before her new husband whisked her away.

At a nearby table Great Aunt Louisa and Mojo were sharing a slice of cake.

Chloe checked her phone again, but no – nothing from Ian.

"Have you thought about doing this professionally?"

She looked up, and was amazed to see the man himself beside her.

"I'm a friend of the groom." He laughed at her astonished expression. "Didn't you know?"

She shook her head, thrilled. He held his hand out and she accepted, letting him pull her onto the dancefloor.

"I was saying," he said, "I think you'd make a great wedding planner."

Wouldn't that be something? After all, she already had all the right connections! (MW)

THE FIRST BOOK I READ...

I was obsessed with *The Worst Witch* by Jill Murphy when I was about seven years old. I found it very comforting to read about a girl who always got everything wrong!

The Captain & Miss Elliot

He was the perfect companion for her troubled soul – but there was something odd about the old seaman

By Peter J. Hedge

The rocks were high, a hundred feet or more above the dark Atlantic waves that crashed in foaming fury along the Welsh coast below her.

A gale was streaming out her raincoat, dress and headscarf like ship's pennants, smarting her eyes and trying to push her back down the path she'd just climbed.

But she stood firm; enjoying with masochistic pleasure the stinging salt and knife-like cold. Still his face smiled at her from every crest, and his voice echoed in the night… vainly calling for her.

Her name was Dawn. Dawn Le Breton, though since the funeral she'd gone back to using her maiden name of Elliott. When a woman is widowed after only six months of marriage, she's hardly had chance to get used to being called "Mrs".

She'd rented a small cottage yards from where she stood. A quiet place, fully furnished, even a dishwasher and TV. Not that she'd eaten much in the past two weeks, the little television she watched forgotten as fast as the picture faded.

Only Sally knew where she was.

"You've got my mobile number – call me any time," she'd said as they hugged at the village's tiny railway station.

"Thanks, Sally," she'd said. "I don't know what I'd have done without you."

"What good are friends if they're only there when they're not needed?" Sally smiled. Then she'd said a strange thing as the guard's whistle sounded and her long journey back to London began. "Don't let me down, Dawn. I trust you, remember. Don't do anything silly, will you?"

"What on earth are you talking about?"

"Just don't betray that trust, Dawn," Sally called as the train slipped away. "If you do get desperate, then call me."

She'd opened her mouth to reply, but then she was completely alone.

The wind dropped a little and the thunder of the ocean sounded even louder. She moved closer, dangerously closer, to the cliff edge and gazed down at the swirling blackness, broken by the pluming spray that the wind tossed about her like raindrops.

For one brief moment, she was tempted to jump: to let the sea that had taken him from her unite them once more. But her friend's faith pulled her back.

She was crying now. "Why?" she asked. But her voice was lost in the wind.

Douglas had seawater in his veins. For as long as she'd known him, the ocean was all he could talk about.

At five it was toy battleships in a tub, Admiral of his tin bath navy. At ten it had been sea cadets with bell-bottoms and weekends visiting warships. Eighteen saw him enter Dartmouth. How grand he'd looked, gold buttons glinting. How proud she'd felt as he was presented with his sword at the passing-out ceremony, the top cadet of his entry.

At twenty-one he was flying, landing and taking off from carriers with a skill and confidence envied by his fellow pilots.

The sea and the sky were the loves of his life, like sirens, calling him to them.

Oh, he'd loved her well. He was kind and gentle, honest and true. No woman could have asked for a better husband.

But his first loves grew jealous, envied her sensuous arms and warm body, the life they were building, the joys they shared. And so they conspired, and destroyed him. Forced him to eject from his stricken fighter, then drowned him.

She stood, her mind filled with memories and visions of what might have been. Wearily she turned from the sea.

It was as she reached the sandy path to the small harbour that she first saw him. The moon slid from behind a cloud and he appeared fifty yards from her, hands clasped behind him, gazing out to sea as she had been doing minutes before.

He was a big man, powerfully built. The duffle coat he wore over a thick roll-neck sweater made him seem even larger.

The hood of his coat lay across his broad shoulders. He seemed unaware of anything except that for which he searched, out at sea.

Long, white, hand-knitted socks turned down over the tops of his gumboots gave him a fisherman's appearance. The fiery red beard, neatly trimmed and pointed, together with his peaked naval cap confirmed it. In forty years, he could've been Douglas. She recognised the stance, the intensity, and the aura of reverence that seemed to radiate from him… but Douglas was no more. He was dead.

As she reached the path he turned, thrust his hands deep into his pockets and stared. For a moment she was afraid.

But he simply watched her walk off towards the stony cottage, then returned his gaze to the moonlit horizon.

Brilliant sunlight awoke her next morning. She'd slept well. For the first time since his death, she'd gone the full night without waking, reaching out for him beside her.

Dawn opened the latticed windows of the tiny cottage and looked out. The sky ➡

was deepest blue, blown clear of clouds by the storm. The sea, calm now, slapped playfully onto the golden sand.

Overhead, terns power-dived the ocean in the relentless search for food and the entire world was peaceful.

She'd start the day with a swim, she decided. The weather and the atmosphere decreed it. Then walk along the beach to the next village, have a shandy in its one pub, marvel at the impossible-sounding Welsh language that everyone in the district spoke so fluently and maybe get a cheese roll.

A pang of guilt made its presence known. She felt better today. Sad, yes – but unhappy and almost suicidal like yesterday? No!

That seemed wrong somehow, to begin to accept her loss and let her heart heal.

With a deep sigh, she put on the yellow bikini she'd bought for their last holiday together a year ago and thought of his laughing eyes. The sun bathed the world with light and through the open window filtered the distant chug of a fishing boat.

The salt water felt good. Very good. As she swam with powerful strokes to a small dinghy moored to a red buoy, it seemed almost as though it were cleansing her, purging the heartache.

She was quite breathless when she reached the boat and clung to its side,

She rolled over, duck-dived and swam underwater towards the beach, surfacing and gulping in clean summer air.

The old seaman from the night before was sitting on one of three large boulders, forearms on knees, a clay pipe in his gnarled hands, watching her emerge.

He was dressed the same, except for his duffle coat. He'd removed his cap and placed it beside him… next to her towel, dress and sandals, spread out in the sun on the second largest rock.

Dawn approached him warily.

"They was floatin' in the water," he said as she reached his side. "Two more minutes an' you'd have lost 'em for good."

He'd anchored them securely with large pebbles and angled the sandals so that the sun reached inside them.

"Oh," she faltered, realising it was the first thing she'd said to anyone in over a week. "Thank you. I'm terribly sorry."

"Nothing to be sorry about, Miss," he said pleasantly. "Just lucky I happened to be passin'." He took an old-fashioned petrol lighter from his pocket, thumbed its large wheel and produced a yellow-blue smoking flame. Then he puffed life into his pipe, finger packing the tobacco as it caught.

She stood awkwardly before him.

"I should rest," he said. "Take an hour. Your clothes'll be dry by then."

"The tide's all wrong today, see. You'd never have made it past the point"

letting her legs float up until her whole body lay on the surface, outstretched, relaxed.

She stayed next to the boat for almost an hour, rising and falling with the sea, mesmerised by its motion. Quite likely she'd have remained all morning had she not suddenly remembered the tide was on its way in and that her shoes, towel and cotton dress lay unprotected in its path.

She hesitated, apprehensive of the old man her mind had already christened The Captain. But it was the logical thing to do.

"Pull up a rock and sit down." He smiled through his beard. "I'm not goin' anywhere and I guess you could use a spot of company."

Instinctively she returned his smile, the doubts and concern she'd had now gone.

The young widow and the Captain remained there until late afternoon. Her dress dried quickly and she slipped it back over her swimsuit.

He talked of the sea, his travels around the world, of foreign land and ships. He fascinated her with his anecdotes of battles and storms, of sea monsters and typhoons, of beautiful native girls and sun-soaked islands.

She told him of her life, though in comparison it seemed dull. But he was a good listener, puffing thoughtfully on his pipe… nodding at this… smiling at that… while she poured her heart out to him.

"Did you ever marry, Captain?"

"No, my dear," he said, laughing. "The sea was my mistress for over fifty years. Now it's too late."

"You sound like Douglas," she said, tracing a D in the sand. "Only he tried to have both a wife and a mistress."

"Did you mind?"

"No," she said. "He was a good husband and a wonderful person. *She* was the one who got jealous."

"Aye. She can be very temperamental."

At six, her stomach began to complain. "It's time I was going," she said standing up, dusting the sand from her dress. "You may not believe this but I had every intention of walking to Llansteffan after my swim this morning."

"That's quite a ways," he said, knocking his pipe out on the heel of his right boot. "But you wouldn't have made it – not along the beach, at any rate. The tide's all wrong today, see. You'd never have made it past the point – not

unless you was up before the sun."

"That's a pity," she said picking up her towel and flapping it. "I was thinking of trying it tomorrow."

"Ah," he said. "Be all right tomorrow. High tide's later. Mind you, you'll have to get your feet wet on the way back – unless you plan finishing in the dark."

"That's great," she said enthusiastically. "I don't suppose you know what the weather will be like?"

"Same as today," he said confidently. "Drop of mist first thing, clearin' nicely. Touch of a breeze. South westerly so you won't get too warm."

Dawn looked affectionately at the Captain. Despite his years, his eyes still carried the glint and sparkle of a man who'd once fluttered many a girl's heart.

"If you're not busy perhaps you'd like to come with me," she suggested, surprised at her impulsiveness.

"I'd like that very much, Miss," he said warmly, stroking his beard. "Not often I get the chance of young company, or any company come to that. Nice to know you're wanted, ain't it?"

Blue-grey eyes looked out squarely from his wizened face – the eyes of an honest man, full of compassion and understanding. They peered into her very soul.

Dawn nodded, unable to speak lest her sudden tears should spill over.

"Shall we say 'bout eightish?" he said cheerfully. "Just here? I've business to attend to in Llansteffan so you'll have to eat by yourself. But we can walk back together."

"That'll be fine. I look forward to it."

"An' so shall I, Miss," he said. "But mind you're not late. I used to be a good swimmer in my day but I've no desire to see how much I've remembered." ➡

"Don't worry, Captain," she laughed. "I'll be here before you are."

He smiled, a little sadly, she thought.

"I doubt that, Miss."

At quarter to eight the following morning the old Captain was sitting comfortably where she'd left him the previous day. He wore the same clothes, or an identical set, and puffed moodily on his pipe as if time no longer had any significance in his life.

"Have you been here long?" she asked.

"No." He smiled, standing up. "But I was here before you thought I'd be."

"Yes you were," she agreed.

"Now," he said. "Let's get walkin' or the tide'll beat us after all."

And so they started off along the beach, the Captain and the girl, widowed less than a year and barely out of her teens. They made a strange couple as they followed the water's edge: he tall, powerfully built; she diminutive, threatening to float away on the light breeze. But they talked like old friends.

The night before, she ate toasted cheese and watching TV. She'd even drunk one of the barley wines Sally had put in the fridge and laughed at her favourite comedian.

But her tears flowed again in bed as his face smiled through her closed lids. The wound was healing, but it still bled.

They followed the same route to Llansteffan the next day, and the day after that. It was very early summer and the few tourists merely looked strangely at her, then continued on their way. Probably because she was an outsider, she concluded.

He always left her before they reached the village. Perhaps, she wondered, he'd done something that had angered the locals,

or simply didn't get on with them. Whatever his reasons he was adamant.

"You go on to the pub," he'd smile, lighting his pipe. "I'll be all right here. I likes to be on my own now and again, and if there are any good-looking young fellows about, you won't need my crusty face frightening them off. I'll be here when you get back…"

And he always was.

She remembered the simple joys of conversation and good company, and began to forget the pain of her bereavement.

At night too, in the tiny cottage, the shattered pieces of her young life seemed to be fitting themselves back together. She phoned friends, talked about her future, laughed a little at their stories and mentioned his name without crying.

She'd seen the brown and white mongrel several times, but paid it no more attention than she would any other dog that enjoyed chasing seagulls.

It was small, resembling a Bassett from the side and a terrier from the front. Its coat was smooth, shiny and it appeared healthy.

Half way through her fourth week, the animal introduced itself. The Captain had just concluded a hilarious anecdote about a run ashore in Shanghai when the dog ran across and began barking.

Dawn stopped in her tracks.

"What's all this?" she laughed. She squatted down. The dog backed away.

"Come on, boy." She held out a hand.

The dog barked, then growled, unsure. It glanced towards a distant outcrop of rocks.

Cautiously, it plodded towards her then licked her hand.

The Captain had resumed walking. She looked up and saw his outline silhouetted by the brilliant sun thirty yards away.

"Wait," she called. "Hang on, Captain!"

The mongrel leapt up, ran towards the rocks, stopped, barked, then ran some more.

It wants me to follow, she thought.

The Captain continued on his way, hands clasped behind his back.

Suddenly irritated by his refusal to wait, she walked towards the dog. It lolloped off, ears flapping, into the outcrop that sprang out of the sand and towered over her.

The animal seemed to have vanished. Annoyed, she turned away.

"Hi, there. Up here. To your left."

Dawn shaded her eyes.

He was about her age, she could tell, despite most of him being concealed behind a large canvas at which he dabbed with one of several brushes.

"Come on up," the stranger said cheerfully, his American accent making his invitation even more attractive. "There's an easy climb if you follow the rock around to the right. Scamp's up and down it all day."

He'd swivelled around by the time she reached him and sat with his back to a boulder, canvas on his knees, palette at his side. He gave her a quick smile.

"Would you mind sitting over there?" He

who say otherwise. I saw you walking along the shore and… there you are."

"But how could you see me from that distance?" she protested, noting the powerful sunburned physique, the ripples of youthful muscle and obvious good looks.

"You can thank Galileo for that." He laughed, noticing her blank expression. "The telescope." He patted a small case beside him. "I've felt quite the… Peeping Tom…?"

"That's right."

He resumed his painting. The sun shone down onto the shimmering ocean and the herring gulls complained noisily. He continued his work glancing frequently at her, but seeing her only as his subject.

"My name's Dawn," she said.

"Great," he replied. "That's what I've called the painting… *The Dawn.*"

"Really? What a strange coincidence. Are you a good artist?"

"Like I said," he laughed. "Somewhere between an aspiring child's matchstick men, and Picasso's abstract bulls. But it keeps me happy." He returned to the painting.

Douglas and the Captain stood in the shadows waiting to be recalled, but she neither saw nor heard them.

"Finished," he declared. Scamp barked.

"Come on up…" His American accent made the invitation even more attractive

nodded towards the edge of the rock where she'd first seen him. "With your back to the sun? I've almost finished."

She settled herself next to Scamp.

"The name's Brett," he said. "Brett Masterton, from San Jose. Hope you don't mind the invasion of your privacy but I've been painting you all week and just need a few details before I've finished."

"Pardon?" she managed to gasp.

"I'm an artist, though there are those

She watched Brett as his lanky frame uncoiled. A feeling she'd forgotten trembled inside her. It was the one she'd had when she'd first seen Douglas in his naval uniform.

He held his painting at arm's length.

"Not bad." As he knelt beside her, she felt the warmth of his personality and shivered as his arm brushed hers.

"Cold?" he asked, concern on his face.

"A little," she lied.

He reached up and pulled down a green ➡

sweater. She felt herself colouring again as his dark eyes stared at her. Hurriedly she pulled on the garment, arranging her hair.

"Suits you." He smiled.

"Well let me see your masterpiece."

He turned the canvas round. "What d'you reckon?" he said. "Be honest."

The picture was beautiful. A girl that could be no one but her, wandering along the deserted beach, eyes searching the sand. The sea was like a looking glass, the sky watery grey. And on the horizon where they kissed, mackerel clouds floated.

"It's marvellous," she whispered.

"Keep it. If you let me buy you lunch, we can pick up a frame."

"Oh no! It's yours."

"Not if I give it to you."

"Then let me pay for it. It's your living."

The young man burst out laughing. "That's great," he managed. "Hilarious."

"What's so funny?"

"I'm sorry, Dawn," he said touching her hand. "I may look the impoverished artist, but nothing could be further from the truth." He let go her hand and touched her cheek.

"My father has a plastics factory in LA," he continued. "I'm going back to run it after my vacation. Painting's just a hobby."

"I see. Then I accept. Thank you."

"You're welcome."

She took the painting from him. "It's just a shame you didn't include the captain."

"Who?" he asked.

"The old man who was with me when Scamp joined us. He was with me every time. I expect he's reached Llan…"

"Dawn – you were by yourself," he interrupted. "Every time I've seen you. That's why I finally plucked up the courage to send Scamp over."

"Don't be daft," she scoffed.

"I'm serious." His expression told her he was. "I've watched you for hours."

A chill ran through her. She shook her head and bit her lip. But the heartache that had slipped into the background returned and she began to sob. He moved closer.

"That's it honey, you cry," he said tenderly as she buried her head on his strong shoulder. "Let it all out."

They sat together, he gently caressing her hair, whispering words of comfort. Eventually her tears ceased. Yet she clung to him, feeling his strength.

"I figured you had a problem," he said quietly. "The way you walked the same route, each day, talking to yourself.

"I don't know who this Captain guy was – or who you thought he was. I guess something pretty bad has happened, and your imagination provided him to help out.

"But Dawn…" He gazed into her tear-stained face. "I'm real, angel. And, if you'll give me a chance, I'll take his place. Today, my shoulder. Tomorrow my heart… if you want."

She gave a wan smile, feeling the firmness of his arms. This was no figment of her imagination.

"I really…"

But the gentle touch of his lips on hers, stopped her sentence, and her memories evaporated into the past with the simple joy of their first kiss. **MW**

THE FIRST BOOK I READ…

Coral Island by the Scottish writer R M Ballantyne was the first novel I read. It was just after I passed my 11+ and in preparation for my grammar school interview.

✦ White flowers have more scent than coloured ones because their ultraviolet patterns are more visible to pollinating insects.

✦ There are over 400,000 types of flowering plant in the world – not counting those not yet discovered, of course.

✦ All parts of the dandelion are edible – and a very good source of vitamins A and C, iron, calcium, and potassium.

✦ The Moon flower only blooms at night.

✦ Vanilla comes from the seeds of the beautiful white vanilla orchid native to Mexico, which was used by Aztecs to flavour their chocolate.

FANCY THAT!

Fascinating facts on **Flowers!**

✦ The name pansy comes from the French word "pensée" meaning remembrance, and in the 19th century the bloom was an ingredient in love potions.

✦ The largest flower in the world – the Titan Arum at up to eight feet tall – smells like a rotting corpse!

✦ Roses may be romantic, but they belong to a family that includes apples, raspberries, cherries, plums, pears, peaches, nectarines and almonds.

✦ The thistle has become Scotland's national flower because in the days of Viking invasions, the Norsemen were slowed down by huge patches of wild thistles.

✦ Broccoli is actually a flower.

✦ In 17th century Holland, tulip bulbs were more valuable than gold!

✦ Angelica, also known as wild celery, has been used for hundreds of years in Europe to cure everything from indigestion to the bubonic plague! Even now it makes a good all-round herbal tea.

It takes 2,000 roses to produce one gram of rose oil

Madame Chocolat?

Mother's Day brought many types of customers, but would her tempting displays bring a man into her life?

By Jan Snook

Spring was always her busiest time of year, Maggie reflected, as she re-filled the basket of chocolate butterflies by the till. Mother's Day, with Easter hot on its heels. She'd really be quite glad when it was over, and for more reasons than one.

It had been just as busy last year, she remembered, but she hadn't been so tired.

The bell tinkled as the door to Madame Chocolat's elegant shop opened yet again – another excited small child accompanied by an indulgent-looking father. Or indulgent husband more like, Maggie thought, smiling automatically at them, and leaving them to wander

mother and mother-in-law. They were in and out of the shop in two minutes flat. School age children would pounce on the chocolate lollipops inscribed with Supermum and hand over their pocket money while their mothers obligingly looked the other way.

The men though were different, like the one who'd come in this time last year. The child with him, whom Maggie soon discovered was called Lucy, must have been about three, and she wanted to buy every confection available. The man discussed the merits of the various boxes seriously with the child, as they walked slowly back and forth along the shelves.

Maggie remembered glancing at her watch. She wanted to get to the bank

The man and the child dithered over the various boxes of chocolates on display

along her beautiful glass shelves where chocolates of all shapes and sizes, decorated with exquisite sugar flowers, were temptingly displayed.

Mothering Sunday brought its own special types of customers, and she catered for them all: middle-aged women would come in, glance around quickly, raise their eyebrows at the prices, and then buy two modest, and often identical, boxes of chocolates – presumably for their

before the lunchtime rush, and it was just on noon. And still they were dithering.

By the time they arrived at a decision, there wasn't a lot Maggie didn't know about the lucky recipient. No, the man assured Lucy, Mummy didn't like dark chocolate. And she probably wouldn't like the chocolate elephant, either, despite Lucy's protestations that anyone would love it. And Mummy hated orange, always had done. ➜

At long last the man came to the counter, bought a chocolate ladybird for the child, and watched as Maggie filled their largest box, directed by Lucy, with the required Mothering Sunday chocolates, tying it with multi-coloured ribbons until even Lucy was satisfied.

He paid what Maggie privately regarded as an extortionate amount without his eyebrows so much as twitching.

Suddenly the shop was empty. Maggie could get to the bank if she really hurried. Jenna, who was busy in the back creating chocolate roses, could be trusted to listen out for the shop bell for a few minutes.

"I'll be as quick as I can," Maggie called, grabbing her jacket and letting herself out of the shop.

There was a hint of spring in the air, and the florist next door had an array of grape hyacinths, tiny narcissi, tulips, daffodils and anemones bursting out of the doorway, their perfume tempting shoppers in.

Maggie gave the florist a wave, feeling the familiar twinge of envy as she stopped to let a man with an enormous bouquet out of the door. It was a long time since she'd had flowers like that. If only things had been different.

Maggie sighed. It was no good looking backwards. It wouldn't bring Edward back. But if only he hadn't stepped onto the zebra crossing at that precise moment… if only the driver of the car had been paying attention…

They would be married by now, maybe with a child. And she would have been celebrating Mothering Sunday herself. Not just helping other people celebrate.

This was ridiculous, Maggie thought crossly as sudden tears threatened. It was five years ago since that ghastly time. She had a good life. A job she loved. She had built up her shop, Madame Chocolat, from nothing. Despite being a Mademoiselle.

Oh for goodness' sake, get a grip!
She was almost at the bank. She reached in her pocket for a tissue. Tears were actually blurring her vision. What had gotten into her?

She was hurrying past a coffee shop, and moved sideways slightly to avoid a woman's shopping trolley and – Oh! – she could feel herself tumbling, hitting the uneven pavement hard. Her cheek was stinging. She put the tissue up to it and found she was bleeding.

"Are you all right?"

"Oh dear, you did go a cropper! Can you get up?"

In no time Maggie was surrounded by concerned shoppers, all offering help and advice. Someone picked up her bag, which she'd dropped. Another tried to help her to her feet, but the High Street was spinning and Maggie put her head in her hands.

"I'm fine," she said for the umpteenth

"Henry, I'll take Lucy inside," she said, waving a hand in the direction of the coffee shop. "while you help this lady. Come and have a warm drink," she urged, looking at Maggie. "You've had a very nasty fall. You need to sit down, you've had a shock."

Henry bent down and helped Maggie up, and the other shoppers gradually drifted away.

"I'm fine, really I am," Maggie protested again, noticing the beginnings of attractive crinkles around Henry's dark blue eyes, and wondering whether Lucy's mother knew how lucky she was.

"No," Henry said with a smile, "you heard Andrea. You've had a shock, and you need a hot drink and a sit down." He frowned. "Is there someone looking after your shop?"

Maggie's face fell. For a moment she had forgotten the shop.

"My assistant's in the chocolate room, the back room where we make the

As he helped her to get up she wondered if his wife knew how lucky she was

time, wishing she wasn't making such a spectacle of herself. "I think I can probably get up now," but when she tried her knee almost buckled. "I'll be OK in a minute," she said, hoping it was true.

"Look Mummy, it's the lady from the chocolate shop," a child said, hopping up and down. "She's hurt herself!"

Maggie looked up to find Lucy's small anxious face peering at her. Behind her were the man she'd already seen and a lovely woman of about Maggie's age – Lucy's mother.

chocolate," she said. "She'll be wondering where I am. I'd really better go. Thank you so much…"

Henry was helping her up, but when she turned to go back to Madame Chocolat's, instead he steered her firmly into the coffee shop, and sat her down next to Lucy.

"I'll just nip back to your shop and tell them what's happened," he said, and was gone before Maggie could object.

A waitress came and took their order, and Andrea smiled. ➜

"Poor you! Henry's always rescuing people… people and animals. And he spends quite a bit of time rescuing me as well, as it happens."

I'll bet he does, Maggie thought.

In the short time she'd seen them together Maggie couldn't help but notice how protectively he watched Andrea. They were a handsome couple, but she did look rather vulnerable, Maggie realised suddenly.

"He climbed up a tree and got my kitten down," Lucy said nodding.

"He's been like that ever since he was a child," Andrea said.

So they'd been childhood sweethearts, Maggie thought, hoping her envy didn't show. Better and better. All she wanted to do was get back to her shop, not to have to play happy families with these people.

But the coffees arrived and so did Henry, so there was no escape.

"Don't tell!" Lucy cried. "It's a secret!"

Maggie's hand flew to her mouth. "Sorry!"

"I don't know what you're talking about," Andrea said, looking up at the ceiling. "Now drink up, Lucy. I need to get you home for lunch – not that you'll have room for it after two chocolate ladybirds."

"Is Uncle Henry coming home with us for lunch?" Lucy asked her mother.

"Not today, Lucy," Henry said, his eyes twinkling. "But I'll see you on Sunday… and I'll bring the secret," he added in a stage whisper.

Uncle Henry? This time Maggie was sure her emotions had been etched on her face in big red letters, because Andrea took one look at her, gulped down her coffee and ushered Lucy out of the café in under a minute.

Henry looked at Maggie. "Sorry, I should have introduced us properly… I'm

Maggie was sure her emotions were etched on her face in big red letters

"Everything's fine," he said cheerily, misinterpreting Maggie's anxious face. "Jenna – is that her name? – was dealing with a customer when I got there. She was totally in control and told me to tell you not to hurry back. So, time for coffee. Oh," he added, fishing a bag Maggie recognised out of his pocket, "and while I was there I bought us each a chocolate ladybird. You need sugar after a shock, after all…"

"You shouldn't be buying me things from my own shop," Maggie objected, horrified. "I should be giving them to you for rescuing me. You've already bought half my stock this morning!"

Henry Fotheringay, and Andrea's my twin sister." He paused. "Most people realise just by looking at us, but maybe not after they've just had a bad fall."

And not when they're so busy envying their happiness that they don't notice how alike they look, Maggie thought.

Maggie couldn't help herself. "So what are the chocolates for?" she asked.

Henry lowered his voice slightly. "Lucy's father walked out when she was a baby. So we usually spend Mothering Sunday together."

"Walked out? On your beautiful sister? And Lucy?"

Henry's face closed. "It amazed us all," he said bitterly. "But I try to keep an eye on them. Help out when I can."

"She's lucky to have you," Maggie said, desperate to ask about his own wife and children, but taking a sip of coffee instead.

"And what about you?" Henry asked, nearly causing her to choke on her coffee. "Where is Monsieur Chocolat?"

"Oh, there isn't one," Maggie spluttered. "I suppose I should have called the shop Mademoiselle Chocolat, but it was a bit too long."

"Really…"

The word hung in the air. It seemed so long since anyone had looked at her in that way that Maggie wondered whether she was imagining it.

"I know we've only just had coffee, but how about some lunch?" Henry asked, still gazing at her.

"I can't just abandon Jenna for any longer. But I would have loved to," she added quickly.

"Dinner then?"

And dinner it was.

What a lot could happen in twelve months! Maggie smiled as she eased herself through the door from the shop to the chocolate room, hoping the bell wouldn't tinkle for a few more minutes. She needed a cup of coffee.

"Any particular reason why you're smiling so smugly?" Jenna said, looking up and smiling herself.

"Oh, you know, just thinking about this time last year."

Jenna laughed, and put the kettle on. Maggie had often wondered how her business had survived those first few months, she'd spent so much time having lunches and dinners, going to the theatre and taking long country walks with Henry. Jenna had been wonderful, always ready to take over the reins.

Then, far sooner than Maggie could ever have hoped, Henry proposed.

"I was going to ask whether you'd consider becoming Mrs Fotheringay," he said, rather shyly, dropping to one knee.

Was? What was coming? Maggie's heart was in her mouth.

"But maybe I should ask instead whether I could become Monsieur Chocolat?"

And the rest, as they say, was history. The shop bell tinkled, and Maggie was brought abruptly back to the present once more.

"Oh, so you're skulking in here, are you?" Henry said, coming into the chocolate room and dropping a kiss on Maggie's head. "I'm glad to see you're sitting down, at least. You shouldn't be overdoing it, you know what the doctor said."

But despite his concern, Henry looked as though he would burst with pride.

"Who knows?" he said, "If they're on time they should be here in time for Mother's Day!"

Yes. Twins. It runs in the family.

. . . .

THE FIRST BOOK I READ...

When I was seven, and living in the States, I was given Charlotte's Web. It's now very old and battered, having been read by my children and grandchildren – we all love it.

Flowers
At Easter

There are a few red faces as well as roses, when the grandchildren dash in while adults tiptoe around…

By Jan Snook

"Here's Othergranny and Grandpa! Look, there's their car! They're getting out!" Four-year-old Amelia turned to Sue, anxious to share her excitement. "Come on, Granny, let's go and open the front door!"

Sue began taking off her apron, hoping that Amelia didn't call her paternal grandmother "Othergranny" to her face. She really should have thought about this earlier, but it was too late to sort it out now.

It was a pity that neither she nor Marilyn – David's mother – was called Grandma or Nana or something else to distinguish them, but by the time Amelia was born they were both called Granny by their other grandchildren, so naturally they were Granny to her too.

Amelia grabbed Sue's hand impatiently. "Come on, quick!" She was beside herself with excitement.

A tiny stab of resentment prickled in Sue's heart. You wouldn't think that she'd been caring for these children week-in, week-out since they were babies. Dealing with cut knees, reading bedtime stories, taking them to get their hair cut…

Chloe, a casserole in her hands, looked at Sue and smiled.

"It's only because they hardly ever see David's parents, Mum. They get just as excited when you arrive. Could you possibly get the door while I just put this

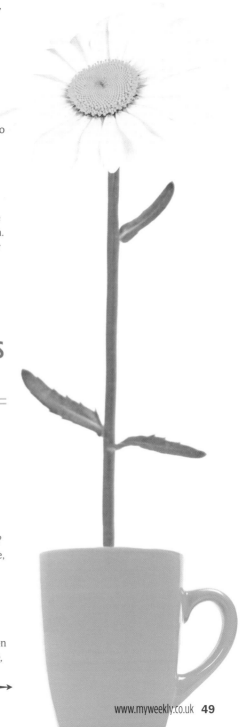

in the oven? David will be down in a mo."

Sue said "Yes, of course" over her shoulder and headed into the hall.

So Chloe had read her mind – or at least her expression – perfectly. Sue felt instantly ashamed of herself. And in any case, it was ridiculous, childish, to feel – what? envious? – of the children's other grandparents. She couldn't bring herself to even think the word "jealous".

And why on earth should she be? She had always regarded it as a privilege to be so much a part of the children's lives, she knew that really. She was just feeling a bit, well, sorry for herself, looking at the happy-looking couple coming up the path. If only Jim were still here to share the joy of grandparenthood.

She must snap out of this right this minute, she thought crossly, and summoned a welcoming smile as she opened the front door.

Worse, Marilyn was incredibly elegant

Amelia's little brother, Barney, had now joined them, and he was tearing up and down the hall to express his delight. Marilyn and Bill came in, their arms full of extravagant Easter eggs and a huge bouquet of flowers, and Sue's heart sank.

When had she last bought flowers for her daughter? she wondered guiltily. Or any sort of hostess present, come to that? Oh dear. And, just to make matters worse, Marilyn was looking incredibly elegant. And here she, Sue, was, in her apron…

"Marilyn! Bill! How lovely to see you both. How was the journey?"

Marilyn gazed at Sue, a brittle smile on her face. *She looks so at home here,* she thought with a pang, taking in Sue's apron. The children, suddenly shy, were ➡

peeping out from behind Sue's skirt. They were obviously perfectly comfortable with her, Marilyn acknowledged.

But they would be. Of course they would. Sue looked after them for a couple of days a week.

Which was a huge commitment, Marilyn reminded herself sternly. She should be very grateful that Sue was able to do it.

And willing, and fit enough. Goodness, she herself was worn out after just a few hours of looking after the children – and Sue did that two days of it every single week – sometimes more. Including taking the dog for a long walk!

Professional childcare was exorbitant these days: if David and Chloe had to pay proper nursery rates, it would hardly be worth Chloe going out to work at all, and

and Chloe set about finding a vase to accommodate the enormous bouquet.

"What a good job it's a long weekend," Marilyn said to break the sudden silence. "David and Chloe look as if they could both do with a rest, don't you think? They're both so busy all the time!"

Yes, I suppose they do," Sue said. To tell the truth, she hadn't noticed. Probably because she saw them so often, she reminded herself. "Mind you, what with girls all having careers and having to juggle work and children and running a house…" Sue tailed off, embarrassed, suddenly remembering that Marilyn's daughter didn't go out to work, but looked after her three young children full-time herself. Maybe she thought Chloe should do the same?

"You mean Othergranny?" Barney's blue eyes were clouded with confusion

the extra money was certainly useful.

"Come on out and say hello, Amelia," Sue was cajoling. "And you, Barney. It's silly being shy when Granny and Grandpa have come all this way to see you, isn't it? Come on now. They've been so looking forward to you arriving," Sue said to Marilyn and Bill as she picked Barnaby up. "They've been talking of nothing else."

Barney immediately buried his head in her shoulder, peeping out at the chocolate eggs, then hiding again.

"I know," Sue said brightly, "why don't you go and get the cards you made? Granny and Grandpa would love to see them."

Barney suddenly slithered down to the floor and scampered off, hastily followed by Amelia.

"Sorry," Sue was saying, taking off her apron, "they'll be OK in a minute."

David went off to get everyone a drink,

Four small feet thundered down the stairs and Amelia and Barney exploded back into the room, their shyness, thank goodness, apparently forgotten. Sue beamed at them in relief and they grinned back at her, then turned their attention to David's parents.

"Here you are, Grandpa," Barney said, running straight at Bill like a guided missile, and talking very fast. "I maked you a Easter card! And 'Melia's maked one for Othergranny!"

Sue hoped to goodness that Bill and Marilyn hadn't caught every word in the rather jumbled speech. But there was no mistaking what Amelia said next.

"I've never seen such great big enormous Easter eggs!" she exclaimed, pointing to the five gigantic chocolate eggs that had appeared on the dining room table, next to Sue's own more modest offerings. "Are they for us, Granny?"

Both Sue and Marilyn started to answer, then laughed.

"Oh dear, us both being called 'Granny' is confusing, isn't it?" Sue said. "We'll have to think of a way round it."

She had tried to talk Bill out of buying such ostentatious eggs, Marilyn thought, gazing at the array of chocolate. But even if they'd bought eggs half the size they would have dwarfed the other gifts on the table.

"They're much much bigger than the ones G…" Barnaby began, but Chloe intervened sharply.

"Granny buys you sweets nearly every week, Barney, and you hardly ever see er… this granny."

"You mean Othergranny?" Barney asked, his big blue eyes clouded with confusion.

"No, Barney. Granny isn't called Othergranny – she's just called Granny." Marilyn caught Chloe glaring at her small son, willing him to understand.

"It's all right Chloe," Marilyn said, smiling ruefully. "I don't mind being called Othergranny – it's very confusing for the children otherwise."

David was handing out glasses of fizz as fast as he could. "It's lovely to see you all," he said, raising his glass, "and here's to a Happy Easter!"

But the children, Sue noted with an inward sigh, were not so easily distracted.

"We call Granny 'Granny'," Amelia began loudly and clearly, "because she looks after us lots of days, and Othergranny… doesn't," she concluded.

"But what about the summer before last, when I'd broken my ankle?" Sue protested indignantly.

"Absolutely," Chloe chimed in, "but I'm afraid Amelia may not remember – and Barney was just a baby…"

"Well," Sue explained to the children, "when I broke my ankle Grandpa and Granny came and looked after you nearly every day, for weeks, even though they live so far away. They certainly stepped in when the need arose. Granny used to…"

"When we need a rose, Granny?" Amelia repeated, puzzled, then nodded to herself. "Rose Granny. OK. Barney and me'll call Othergranny 'Rose Granny' instead."

"Well – I'm very honoured, that's a very pretty name," Marilyn agreed.

Barnaby was nodding.

"Rose Granny who comes sometimes, and Granny who comes here on lots of dayses."

Amelia smiled at Sue.

"That's right – you can be Daisy Granny," she said, "because you come lots of days. Rose Granny and Daisy Granny. Then we won't get mixed up." She nodded to herself with satisfaction.

"Trust the children to sort it out," David said happily. "Another toast is in order, I think – here's to Rose and Daisy and a very Happy Easter to both the flower grannies!" Ⓜ

Off To Pony School

How could my infuriating little sister and her plastic ponies possibly help me with my life's ambition?

By Celia Kay Andrew

How I wanted a room that I didn't have to share with my ten-year-old sister Claire! Ever since Grandpa came to live with us, I'd been lumbered with her.

Mum said it wouldn't be forever and I did love Grandpa (and Claire too, really) but after a whole year of My Little Pony and all those stupid pink dolls scattered over my computer and bookshelves, I'd had enough.

My exam results weren't very good and I was sorry for Mum and Dad's sake,

but let's face it, I'd never been academic. It didn't help that Claire was really bright.

"Never mind, Mandy, I expect you'll get a job breaking up horses," she said cheerfully, watching me shift three pink plastic ones off my bedside table.

"Breaking in," I corrected through gritted teeth. She did it deliberately, getting things like that wrong.

Everyone thought she was hilarious. They should try living with her.

She knew I was desperately keen to get a job that was involved with horses. My part time helping-out at the local horse dealing, trekking and riding stables wasn't

something my parents were keen on as a career prospect ("no future there, unless you own the place") but it had certainly taught me to ride everything and anything that moved under saddle.

"I'll help you find a job," Claire said, to make up for her deliberate tease. She pulled out the two-week-old *Horse And Hound* magazine from under my bedside lamp. "They've got lots of jobs in here, at the back, look –"

As though I hadn't read it over and over again.

"Mandy!" Mum called from downstairs. "It's Mrs Dean from the trekking stables on the phone, she wants to know if you'd like to take a ride out this afternoon."

"She can't," Claire grumped. "She's coming to the hospital with me."

I spoke to Mrs Dean and said no, because I'd promised Claire I'd go with her to her heart check-up. She always had to have bloods taken and she hated it. Mum couldn't bear to see her upset, so when they took the blood, I always went in with Claire instead, to gag her and hold her down while she yelled her head off… no, that's not fair. She was really brave and only made faces and screwed her eyes shut. ➡

When they first found out about her heart, they had to test the oxygen or something from an artery in her wrist and she used to cry and get into such a state she nearly lost consciousness.

But once they'd done the operation and remodelled her heart on a normal human one (joke, sorry) she was much better about the horrid tests.

"Thanks," she said gruffly, as we got into the car. "You're too good for them anyway. You should be riding those thoroughbreds up the road."

"Those thoroughbreds" were the wonderful, beautiful lean racing machines at the local National Hunt racing trainer's yard. You had to be sixteen even to be considered for a job there, and you had to prove you could ride. Well, I'd just turned sixteen and I knew I could ride pretty well, so I'd written to Mr Jamieson (PJ to those in the know) and was waiting for a reply. They'd got some staff accommodation, too, and it was so close Mum wouldn't mind me living there.

Claire got the all-clear from the consultant and was given another appointment for six months' time. She gabbled about the sponsored ride we had arranged with the Pony Club for the first Saturday of the Easter holidays in aid of the heart unit that had operated on her, and the consultant solemnly handed my mother a tenner and signed Claire's sponsorship form.

"You're one of our success stories, so I'd better cough up," he said.

We visited the trekking yard on the way home, to drop me off so I could help out at evening stables with the two ponies we had loaned over the winter. The fresh air and riding had really brought life and colour back into Claire's cheeks but she wasn't really pony-mad – she liked brushing ponies that I'd already knocked the mud off, and giving them their buckets of feed, but she absolutely hated going out in the rain and she point-blank refused to muck out the stables. In fact her idea of pony-life was really those wretched pink things in our bedroom.

"Your loan-time is up at Easter, but not until after the sponsored ride," Mrs Dean reminded me. "Pablo's due for shoeing next week – tell your dad to leave that one to us." She looked me up and down. "Next winter you'll have to take something bigger, you're getting a bit big for Pablo."

Next winter was a long time away. I'd have to get a job before then, and goodness knows if I'd have any time to have a winter loan pony.

And I somehow doubted that Claire would be much interested if she had to do all the work on her own!

The day of the sponsored ride came. There were four of us from the trekking centre. The hired lorry drove us up the Tarmac road through the deer park of the magnificent Carrington Manor for the sponsored ride.

My ten-year-old sister bounced on her seat and wound down the window.

"Mrs Pig's-Horn! I'm here! We can get started now!"

"Pinkthorne, Claire," I corrected, as we pulled up beside a large horsebox with *Regal Showjumpers* painted on the side. "You must not call her Mrs Pig's-Horn."

The Regal ponies were tied around their transport with a host of very upmarket children busy saddling them up.

"Wow," murmured Claire, wide-eyed. "They're a bit posh." She shoved open the door and scampered across. She was soon talking to another equally excited ten-year-old, introducing herself.

"It's my ride! We're raising money for my heart unit. I nearly died. Mrs Pig's-Horn said the Pony Club would help raise money for them. How much have you been sponsored for?"

The smell of horse, crushed turf and leather was gorgeous in the sharp spring morning air. I could hear the other ten-year old loudly showing Claire round the inside of the transporter. Her crystal accent bragged, "These are all racing shoes – they're called plates, you know – from famous steeplechasers. We hang all our red rosettes from them… "

"Not many up there now," Claire's voice pointed out. her voice coming from the open living space window.

"Daddy takes most of them down,"

She saw where I was looking.

"Didn't you check?" Her face went very red. "Well, I'll just have to take him without a beastly shoe!"

"No way," I said firmly. "He'll never make ten miles like this."

"What, then?" Her voice was quavery.

I went to find Mrs Pinkthorne, down at the start. The stewards had gathered round her, fluorescent Sam Brownes over their riding jackets.

"Hello, Mandy," Major Rossiter boomed at me. "Is young Claire looking forward to her ride?"

"Well, she was, "I told him glumly. "Except her pony's lost a shoe."

"No problem!" His moustache quivered. "My nephew Mike is here. He's a farrier. I'll send him over."

Of course it was too good to be true. When the nephew turned up at our lorry, he examined Jasper, shaking his head. "I've got my tools, but I'd need the shoe."

Claire appeared, tie askew, pigtails at different heights, filched lolly in hand

came the crystal-cut reply, coolly patronising. "Too many."

Bloomin' show-off, I thought. Red rosettes are Firsts, but some places have blue ones as Firsts. I'd won a few green ones (fourths) and pink ones (fifths). And that was only for little gymkhana races, not the Regal Showjumpers' proper affiliated show jumping classes.

I bawled at Claire to come and give me a hand as I went to unload our ponies.

"Oh no!" I stared in horror. Claire appeared, tie askew, pigtails at different heights and a lolly in her hand, undoubtedly filched from the Regal crew. She was full of bubbles and burbles.

"That lot are stiff rich, their horsebox is like a palace –"

Claire was clearly in love.

"Leave Jasper here. I'll ride in front of you, on your horse."

"You're a fast worker!" He gave a shout of laughter, showing very white teeth. Oh, my sister was embarrassing!

It was quarter to ten and we were meant to leave on the hour. The Regal ponies had all gone down to the starting area. I shrugged at Mike Rossiter, feeling wretched.

"She's been looking forward to it for months," I said, watching Claire haring off to goodness knows where. "She's forced everyone from the local vicar to the racing trainer Peter Jamieson to sponsor her."

"I know." He gave his gorgeous laugh again. "I work for PJ and he told me ➔

about her. He insisted I came on the ride too, on his old hack."

"You do the racehorses?"

Mike nodded. "Some of them. "He picked up Jasper's hoof again. "He can't do ten miles without a shoe. Sorry."

"Won't have to!" Claire reappeared, breathless, a grin like a melon slice on her face. "Oh, do hurry, use this, it'll fit!" She held a bright red horseshoe in her hand.

With a sinking heart I knew exactly where she had found it. Bemused, Mike took it. "It's a racing plate," he said.

"Off Desert Orchid," nodded my dreadful little sister, totally unabashed and unashamed. She frowned slightly. "Or was it Red Rum?"

I went slowly round to the side of the Regal Show Jumpers' transporter, climbed the step and peeped inside the living area. Several red rosettes were lying loose on the draining board and there was a horseshoe-shaped space in the paintwork on the wall. Oh, God.

Just as slowly, I made my way back to the spot where Claire and Mike and our ponies were waiting.

"I'll put it back later. After." Claire was looking at Mike, hopping with impatience. Wordlessly he picked up Jasper's foot and measured the shoe against it.

"It will do, just for a while," he said. He unpacked his tools and set to work.

The Carrington Manor Ride was great fun. Claire and Mike and I rode together and everyone, even the horses and ponies, had a lovely time trotting and cantering through the glorious open parkland. Claire never stopped yattering all day, and the story of Jasper's bright red shoe caused a lot of giggling and laughter.

The Regal parents were waiting for us, grimly, when we returned.

Before a scene could start, a local

reporter came rushing up to interview Claire and laughingly insisted on photographing the no-longer-red horseshoe attached to her pony's hoof. He was so enchanted by the story that he completely missed the frost in the Regal parents' tones and he shook their hands, congratulating them on saving the day.

They started to smile, jollied out of their annoyance by Claire's hugs and general joyfulness.

"Think of the splash headline!" the reporter hooted. "*Heart girl uses brain to shoe horse!*"

"*Heart girl gets brained by big sister,*" I said aside to Mike Rossiter darkly.

"*Heart girl's sister gets job interview.*" He grinned at me and tapped his mobile. "Just reported back to PJ and mentioned you. He wants to see you first thing in the morning. I reckon you'll get that job, Mandy."

My mouth opened. And shut.

"Oh, cool! Magic!" I glanced across at my sister. "Er – this would be living-in?"

"Sharing a cottage with three other girls," said Mike.

"Wicked!" I watched Heart Girl winning over the Regal parents who were now laughing and joking no more talk of "wilful damage and theft".

I hugged Mike. "Oh, thank you. You've just made my day as well as Claire's."

Claire, sharp as a blooming tack, must have overheard and, grabbing credit as only she could, called over, "I told you I'd help you find a job with horses!" ⓂⓌ

THE FIRST BOOK I READ...

One beloved early novel was *Shadow The Sheepdog*, a present for my seventh birthday from my parents. My father was a vet and all my favourite books had animals in them.

Brain Boosters

Kriss Kross

Try to fit all the listed words back into the grid.

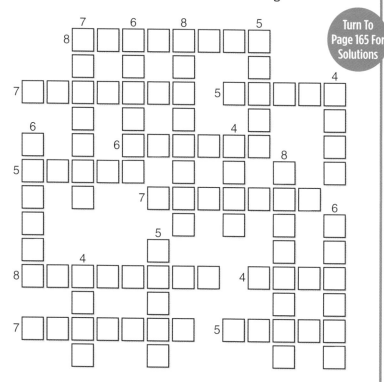

Turn To Page 165 For Solutions

4 letters	5 letters	6 letters	7 letters	8 letters
Ibex	Ankle	Castle	Bouquet	Isotonic
Need	Bower	Emigre	Liberty	Premiere
Opus	Eyrie	Fallow	Proviso	Stripper
Taut	Groan	Rookie	Provoke	Withhold
	Shell			

The Magic Words

To Jamie, it was almost as if there was a secret message in the old lady's repeated phrase...

By Jo Styles

Take care. Peggy said it again this morning," Jamie said as he limped across the lounge.

"*Take care*," he repeated, mimicking the elderly lady who lived next door. "I was a bag of nerves all day. I thought I'd got away with it until I came home from

his comic books from the coffee table and waved it at him.

"You don't think you've been reading too many of these, do you? Or watching too many of those weird films you like?"

"Now you're being ridiculous."

"Oh, *I'm* being ridiculous." She wrapped her arm around him and kissed his cheek. "My poor baby," she soothed.

"A few bad things? It's more than a few. Peggy's stealing all my good luck"

work Then I tripped over my own foot and fell off the bus. Please don't grin at me like I've gone insane."

Becky, his girlfriend, sat on the sofa. She pulled her lips down with her fingers.

"Is that better?"

"No, it's not." Jamie flopped down next to her and rubbed his sore ankle. "Peggy's jinxing me." He frowned as Becky's eyebrows rocketed skyward. "Fine, fine – you explain my run of bad luck, then. I've lost my wallet twice and keys three times. I ruined my favourite shirt snagging it on that fence. Explain to me how I accidentally sent that email to my boss. Go on, explain that."

Becky shook her head. "So a few bad things have happened lately…"

"A few?" Jamie crossed his arms. "It's more than a few. Peggy's out to get me. She's stealing all my good luck. "

Becky picked up one of

"In the wars. Again. I suppose it's my turn to make the dinner?"

Jamie stroked his injured ankle.

"Chips might be nice. I'd help but…"

"…but you have missed the sofa, having been away from it all day and you have so much to tell it?" Becky gave a sad little smile. "Yes, yes, I know. You're hurt." She gave him another hug. "And besides – with your luck you might just set the house on fire."

The next morning, Jamie opened the front door a crack and peered out.

He'd have to make a dash for it. The pain in his ankle had subsided overnight but he'd neglected to tell Becky that. A little bit of limping had really brought out the best in her.

The drive looked clear so a mad charge into the street looked in order. He definitely didn't want Peggy launching *Take Care* at him again. Those two little words had definitely become the harbingers of doom ever since he moved in with his girlfriend.

Jamie closed the door quietly, whirled about and surged towards the pavement.

"Hello Jamie, lad!" Peggy's reedy voice stopped him as dead as a traffic light on red. "Working on Saturdays now, then?"

"Oh, hello, Peggy." ➝

Peggy stood half-hidden by her privet hedge. Stick-thin with wispy white hair, the creepy old lady's eyes were such a pale shade of blue that they sometimes looked almost white.

"Yes, yes, I'll be working on Saturdays for the next few months."

"How's Becky? I haven't seen her for a day or two. You dropped lucky finding her, didn't you?"

"Yes… yes, I was very lucky. She's fine. Just fine."

Peggy smiled for an eerily long time.

"Oh, I haven't told you, have I? I had some good news yesterday. One of my scratch cards won me a hundred and fifty-two pounds."

"Really? That's great." *Was that my*

Jamie had accidentally dispatched to him instead of Becky. It had included a postscript. *PS. My boss is such a toad he's even started to sound like one. Ribbit.*

"You're on notice, Jamie," his boss had yelled after calling him in to his office. The email sat stark and condemning on the computer screen he made a point of turning round. "I want you in on Saturdays for the next six months. Is that clear?"

"Yes, Mr Granger," Jamie had agreed meekly. "That's as clear as crystal."

Now Jamie stood at the bus stop wavering. There was a fifteen-minute gap between buses. If he arrived late that morning, he'd get fired. Maybe it'd be better if he didn't arrive at all?

He frowned. Had Becky's usual sunny smile wobbled a little at his words?

luck you stole, by any chance?

"I thought I might try the betting shop next. I don't know the first thing about horses like my late husband, but when you're having a run of good luck you ought to use it, don't you think?"

"Oh, yes – of course you should. Well, I must be off or I'll miss my bus."

"All right, Jamie. Take care."

Take care – she'd said again! Jamie swallowed dryly as Peggy ambled back up her path. *It's all in your head,* he told himself. *It's all comic books, bad films and an overactive imagination.*

Jamie's bus went screaming by the bus stop long before he reached it.

He checked his watch. *Oh, it was early, while you were right on time. It's definitely all in your head.*

His boss wouldn't be in the mood for excuses, not after reading the email

B ecky," Jamie wailed when he reached home once more. He slammed the front door closed. "Becky? I'm back."

Where was she? He hurried to the kitchen window. There she was hanging out the washing. Peggy leaned on the fence giggling away.

Jamie frowned. *So what's so funny?*

"Becky!" he yelled down the garden.

"Jamie?" She came scurrying up the path. "What's the matter? Why aren't you at work?"

Jamie pouted. "My ankle feels so much worse," he lied. "I was trying to be brave going on to work but I've made it much worse now. Can you ring my boss and tell him I won't be in this morning?"

He leaned on her like a crutch as she helped him back inside.

"Take care, Jamie" sailed over his shoulder as Peggy waved. Jamie shuddered, pushing the back door closed.

"Peggy was telling me how her anniversary's coming up." Becky pulled ice cubes out of the freezer. "Do you know how long she would have been married to her husband if he'd lived? Fifty-five years. She said they married when they were eighteen. Eighteen. Imagine that. She says they shared everything."

"Lucky them. Ouch. Ouch." Jamie winced as Becky rolled up his trouser leg and pressed the ice, now wrapped in a tea towel, against his bare flesh.

"It doesn't look swollen to me," she observed.

"It's probably the ligament," he replied. "Can you ring my boss now? I'm in enough trouble with him as it is."

Becky kissed his cheek. "Of course I will."

"Can you help me to the sofa first?"

"Of course I can."

"Don't worry," Jamie added valiantly as he hobbled along. "Carry on with whatever you were doing; I won't get in your way."

He frowned. Had Becky's usual sunny smile wobbled just a little?

Later that morning, the vacuum cleaner grumbled away upstairs. The washing machine sang along in the kitchen, doing a cup-rattling duet with the dishwasher.

Just a normal Saturday then, Jamie thought. He lay on the sofa in the lounge, his eyes sliding shut. *I really need a coffee.*

"Becky?" he yelled. "Becky!"

She obviously couldn't hear him over all the noise. He heaved himself upright and padded into the kitchen. He filled up the kettle, set it to boil and then went on a biscuit raid.

He'd just pulled a packet of chocolate digestives from the cupboard when he turned and saw Becky standing in the doorway, a duster in her hand.

"Oh, there you are." Becky carried on staring. "What's up?"

"I thought you were a cripple, but you just about did a pirouette just then."

"Oh." *Oops.* "Oh, my ankle feels a bit…better. That's all. It must have been your ice pack. You're such a good…"

"…nurse, cleaner, gardener, cook, personal shopper, taxi driver, electrician and mechanic," she tagged on in a tight voice.

Jamie frowned. "Sorry?"

"Was your ankle really hurt at all? Or did you just want a little bit more attention?"

"Attention? What? No!" he said indignantly.

"You know, ever since you moved in here all I do is give, give, give and all you do is take, take, take."

"That's not true!"

Becky crossed her arms.

"Isn't it? I think it is. When did all this nonsense about being jinxed start? Oh yes – I remember. It was after I started going out on my own with my friends a couple of times a week, wasn't it? It must be so awful for you, Jamie, being here all on your own, having to do things for yourself. You'd have to get off the sofa, for a start. You know, I think Peggy's right about you."

"Peggy… Peggy said something to you about me, did she?"

"Yes – she said you seemed a bit lazy and a tiny bit immature."

Jamie gawped. "Me… immature?"

Becky cocked her head.

"Yes, immature enough to blame a run of bad luck on some wild, crazy idea, for example. I'm starting to think you moving in with me was a very bad idea."

"No, it wasn't." Jamie's head started to swim. "I love you."

Becky snorted. "I don't believe you. ➙

I'm going to pack. I'm going to stay with my sister for a few days. When I come back, I don't want you or any of your things to still be here."

"Becky. No," Jamie wailed.

Take care, Peggy had yelled at him from the garden just before his luck had snapped clean in two. He stood shaking as Becky thundered back up the stairs.

"Becky. Please," Jamie said later as Becky angled her suitcase out of the front door and onto the drive. "I'll start doing my share of chores. I'll change. I will. I promise. I love you."

Becky's lip quivered. "How can you love someone and expect them to run around after you night and day?"

"I just… I didn't realise how much I wasn't doing. Honestly, Becky."

"Is everything all right?" Peggy peered over her privet hedge. "Oh." She stared down at Becky's fat suitcase. "Are you off somewhere, love?"

Becky wiped tears from her cheeks. "I'm just off to my sister's."

"Oh well, take…"

"Don't you dare tell her to take care!" Jamie cut in. "I've never known anybody pass on as much bad luck as you do, Peggy. If you want to ruin somebody's life then carry on making a mess of mine, but don't you dare start picking on my Becky. Don't you even think about it."

Peggy blinked at him like a startled deer as Jamie stood in front of his girlfriend, his arms spread wide as if willing to shield her from whatever the old woman might muster next.

"Jamie. You're being ridiculous." Becky said from behind him. "There isn't

a jinx on you. Don't be silly. But…but…" Warm had seeped into those words.

Jamie turned about. A smile brightened Becky's face, her cheeks flushing as she stared up at him.

"That was really sweet of you, trying to look after me like that. I mean, taking on evil forces… even if they don't exist… nobody's ever done that for me before."

Jamie stood holding his breath. It looked as if Becky stood holding hers too. "Please," he said. "Can we talk? I'll do my share from now. I will. I might be lazy and immature… but I do love you. "

Becky's expression softened even more.

"Maybe I was a bit hasty back there."

Peggy chuckled.

"That's the way, you two," she said. "A bit and give and take, that's what keeps the magic alive."

The what? The magic? Jamie's head snapped around. He stared into the old woman's light blue eyes.

It's all in your head, he warned himself as Becky's hand slipped into his own. They both stepped back, then, as something dark flashed by their feet.

Impossible. Peggy didn't own a black cat… or did she?

The old lady gave another laugh.

"You go and… *take care*… of each other." She added to her words a knowing little wink. "Nothing bad will ever happen to either of you as long as you do that." ⓜ

THE FIRST BOOK I READ…

The Pullein-Thompson sisters – Josephine, Diana and Christine – wrote books about the kind of horsey adventures I wanted to go on but my parents couldn't afford.

✦ The word candle is derived from the Latin word "candere", meaning to shine.

✦ The oldest candle manufacturers still in existence are Rathbornes Candles, founded in Dublin back in 1488!

✦ Tea lights are now the most frequently purchased type of candle, followed by votives and then container candles.

✦ Magic candles will re-ignite even after being blown out. This is achieved by mixing red phosphorus into the wax.

✦ The Yankee Candle Company uses over 1.2 million metres of wick each year – that's the same distance as between Bristol and the Shetland Islands!

FANCY THAT!

Fascinating facts on **Candles!**

✦ A candle flame has two regions: the bluer, hotter region near the wick burns hydrogen and oxygen to produce water vapour, and the brighter yellow region produces carbon dioxide by oxidising carbon.

Beeswax candles are naturally dripless

✦ The trend among dinner guests now is to arrive with candles as gifts, rather than wine, chocolates or flowers, because "they last longer".

✦ According to figures from market analysts, sales of scented candles reached a staggering £89m in 2012.

✦ Surveys suggest that about 96% of candles are bought by women – and 35% of candles are bought during the Christmas period.

✦ Candles were the primary source of artificial light in the world until as late as the 1990s.

✦ Ancient Greeks decorated cakes with candles at the temple of Artemis, to represent the moon. It didn't become a birthday tradition until the late 1700s.

✦ Candlemakers have reported a big increase in demand as Brits spend more evenings at home because of the depressed economy.

Carrie's Candle Tree

From a conker seed their love took root and their family
grew as strong and beautiful as the chestnut tree...

By Elaine Chong

There's a saying – "Mighty oaks from little acorns grow" – only in Carrie's case, it was a horse chestnut tree and a conker.

She spotted the tiny sprout with its unmistakeable starfish-shaped leaves growing next to the road and, out of nothing more than a sense of curiosity, gently pulled it from the soil.

"I couldn't believe it," she told me later. "This huge conker suddenly popped out of the ground." She planted it in a large terracotta pot and put it out on the balcony of our one bedroom flat, which overlooked a sprawl of busy streets.

"It won't grow," I told her.

"It's already growing," she said. "I've just transplanted it."

"Well, if does grow, we can't keep it here," I protested. "It's a tree. What are we going to do with tree?"

She laughed. "We'll just have to move somewhere with a garden."

Over the course of the following year, the "sprout" increased in size – and so did Carrie. With our first baby on the way, we gladly waved goodbye to the cramped flat we'd shared since we left college, and moved out of town to a house with a good sized rectangle of garden behind it.

Carrie insisted that the little tree come with us. It was still growing in its terracotta pot but spidery threads of root escaped from the holes in the bottom. Just like us, it needed more space.

"Are you seriously going plant it in the garden?" I asked her. I'd done my homework in preparation for what I thought might be a difficult conversation, and I gave her the facts and the figures. "Horse chestnut trees can reach 30 metres in height with trunks 2 metres wide!"

She laughed. "They can also live up to 300 years." Her face suddenly went all dreamy. "In some countries, they call them candle trees. I think that's so romantic."

"What about the foundations?" I said, pointing at the brickwork.

"It'll be fine," she said. "I'll plant it well away from the house."

In spite of my dire warnings and loud protestations, a large hole was dug at the far end of the garden and the little tree found a new home.

Over the next four years, the tree and our family increased in size, but with baby number three on the way, it was time to uproot ourselves once again and find somewhere with even more room. We scoured the estate agents' windows and eventually found what we hoped would be our forever home.

"It's perfect," Carrie told me. "It's got a huge garden – room for the children to play and space to plant a big veggie plot. always wanted to grow vegetables." A smile tugged at the corners of her mouth. "There's even space for my tree."

For a few seconds, I looked at her uncomprehending, and then it hit me. "You cannot be serious!" I exclaimed.

"Why not?" she said. "You told me it would grow too big for this garden."

"We are absolutely, definitely *not* taking that tree with us when we leave!"

It took an excavator to dig it up. It took a small truck to move it. And the tree surgeon who supervised the procedure warned Carrie, "It won't survive."

That was thirty years ago.

I'm standing at our bedroom window. Night is gathering at the corners of the garden, casting shadows onto the lawn. The air is warm and full of the fragrance of flowers in bloom.

In the middle of the lawn, Carrie's horse chestnut trees lights up the darkness like a giant candelabra. When the tree blossoms, every evening feels like a celebration. But this night is a celebration. It's our ruby wedding anniversary. Below us, the whole family has gathered. Today there are children and grandchildren, everyone is here.

Behind me, the bedroom door opens and Carrie walks in and joins me at the window, slipping her hand into mine. "Are you admiring my tree?" she asks.

"I'm admiring everything that my wonderful wife of forty years has created here," I tell her as I draw her into my arms and hold her close to my heart. 🅜

Off The Menu

Joanne playing matchmaker for her brother had a strange effect on him… and on his appetite!

By Lin Silver

It's Boxing Day today, isn't it Mum?" Jack giggled as Joanne took the beef out of the fridge.

"You know very well it isn't," Joanne said crossly.

"But it must be," Ben interjected, with feigned astonishment. "I mean, you're doing the Feast of Stephen, aren't you?"

"Will you drop this, you two?" Joanne muttered. "The joke's worn very thin now. It wasn't even that funny to start with."

"Well, it does have a grain of truth," Terry said, coming in from the garden."How many roasties are you doing? There's enough to feed an army in that saucepan!"

"Mum is going to feed an army," Jack laughed. "The army of worms in Uncle Stephen's stomach!"

"I'm warning you," Joanne said sternly.

comfort eating. I can't just tell him we don't want him round anymore."

"How about making smaller portions?" Terry suggested, secretly admiring his wife's soft heartedness.

"He'll just ask for seconds, or raid the larder," Joanne sighed. "He never used to be like this. It's only because of Claire."

"Isn't there another way of stopping him pigging out?" Terry said. "For instance, couldn't we say we're all on strict diets now and preparing enormous banquets is impossible because of the temptation?"

Joanne glanced down at her slim figure and Terry's own trim physique.

"He's not stupid!" she said.

"OK," Terry sighed. "Onto Plan B."

"What's Plan B?" Joanne asked.

Terry shrugged.

"Don't know. There isn't one yet. If only he'd find another woman."

"Your brother needs a lonely woman who can cook for him," Ben said

"Sorry Mum," said Ben, not sounding sorry at all. The boys ran off to their room and Joanne began mixing the batter.

"Really, love, they do have a point," Terry said, taking off his gardening boots. "Your brother's a nice enough chap, but he eats us out of house and home when he comes to visit."

Joanne sighed.

"I know. But he's been like a lost sheep since Claire left him and I think he's

"Like who?" Joanne replied. "Delia Smith? Nigella?"

"There must be plenty of lonely women out there who'd be only too happy to cook for him," Terry mused.

Joanne suddenly leapt to her feet.

"I know someone!" She cried. "Maggie Stowe, who lives opposite the church. She's a singleton and a fantastic baker as well. She makes cakes for all the school fetes. She just loves cooking so they could

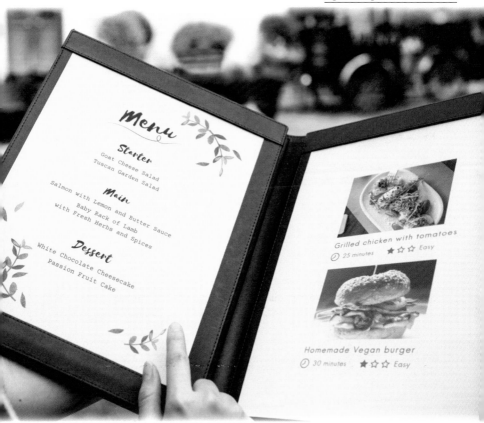

be a match made in Heaven."

"Great, but how are we going to get them together?" Terry asked.

"Leave it to me," Joanne said, with a crafty gleam in her eye.

Two weeks later they were all sitting round the dining table, politely waiting for Stephen to finish. They had a long wait as Stephen polished off everything.

Ben kept humming, *Good King Wenceslas*, totally ignoring Joanne's ferocious warning look.

"What's that you're singing, lad, it's not Christmas!" Stephen said, dabbing gravy from his chin.

"But I could be *Good King Wenceslas*,"

Ben said cheekily. "Looking out on The Feast Of –"

"Boys! You can leave the table!" Joanne shouted, and they scarpered immediately, laughing their naughty little heads off. She turned to Stephen and sighed. "Sorry about them."

"No matter," Stephen said. "What's for dessert, Jo?"

The moment had come to put her plan into action.

"Oh, heavens, I forgot to tell you – there isn't one today. I had a crisis in the kitchen and it ended up in the bin."

"What? No pud?" Stephen gasped, dismayed.

Joanne played her ace.

"Don't panic. I have a friend just up ➔

the road who's a brilliant cook, and she said you're welcome to pop round and pick something from her stock."

"I'd best get round there, then, if you're sure she won't mind," Stephen said, levering himself from the table.

The moment they were alone, Terry and Joanne did a triumphant high-five.

"Let's hope Maggie turns out to be his dream woman!" Joanne said.

Her hopes were dashed when Stephen returned in less than ten minutes with a sticky-toffee pudding and his face buried in a large handkerchief.

"Cats!" he bellowed, between sneezes.

"What about them?" Joanne asked.

"I'm allergic to them!" Stephen sniffed, mopping his florid face. "Maggie's lovely and we were having a great chat while I picked out a pud, but then her cat Tizer came in and I was finished." He sneezed again. "What time will tea be?"

"That's it, then," Terry murmured as he and Joanne started the washing up. "Mission failed."

However, Stephen's next visit turned out to be a big surprise. A very different man turned up that day, most notably because he hardly ate a thing.

"Are you all right, Stephen?" Joanne asked, concerned.

Her brother sighed deeply. "I'm fine, just not very hungry I'm afraid."

Joanne was glad Stephen didn't see the looks of exaggerated shock on the faces of her two boys.

"I think it's the tablets," Stephen said, pushing a roastie round his plate.

Joanne's jaw dropped. "Are you ill?" she asked. "You do look as if you've lost weight."

Stephen shook his head. "No, they're

tablets to stop my allergy to cats," Stephen replied. "Truth is, I'd really like to see that friend of yours again, Maggie, and the only way that can happen is if I can cope with that ginger monster of hers winding itself round my legs!"

Terry and Joanne exchanged covert expressions of delight.

"Actually, if you don't mind, I might trot along there now and see if she's in," Stephen said, rising from the table and leaving half a dinner unfinished – something totally unheard of. "No time like the present!" He laughed, slightly embarrassed at confessing his interest in Maggie.

"Oh, I'm sure she'll be thrilled to see you!" Joanne said, winking at Terry.

"Let's just hope Maggie does feel the same way about him," Terry said, with fingers crossed when Stephen had gone.

"Oh, I'm sure she does," Joanne replied confidently.

Now she understood why Maggie had struck up an unusually long conversation with her when they'd bumped into each other at the supermarket, casually asking when Stephen would visit next.

It also explained why Maggie had mentioned Mrs Parkes from number thirty and asked if Joanne knew if she still did occasional cat-sitting, just on the off-chance Stephen should like to call round, of course, so they might get to know each other better… **MW**

RECIPE AND FOOD STYLING: KATHRYN HAWKINS PHOTOGRAPHY: LIGHTHOUSE PHOTOGRAPHY

Coconut Ice Christmas Trees

Ingredients (Makes 8)

- ◆ **135g ready-to-roll white icing, chopped**
- ◆ **1tsp good quality vanilla extract**
- ◆ **Green food colour gel or paste**
- ◆ **65g desiccated coconut**
- ◆ **White piping icing and festive decorations, to decorate**

1 Put the icing in a saucepan with 2tsp water. Heat gently until melted, then stir until well blended. Remove from the heat and mix in the vanilla and sufficient colour to make a pretty green shade.

2 Working quickly, mix in the coconut to form a stiff paste. Line a board with baking parchment. Divide the mixture into 8 portions and form each into a small cone about 6cm tall. Leave in a cool place until firm.

3 To decorate, pipe icing on to the trees and decorate with festive shapes and sugar balls.

The Top Of The Class!

Tamara was determined to overcome her own shyness to help her pupil – as was the little boy's father

By Paula Williams

Tamara Wytchford stood at the front of the class and smiled at the shining Monday morning faces looking up at her.

"Good morning, Jupiter Class," she said cheerfully.

"Good morning, Miss Wytchford," Jupiter class chorused back at her, as of one voice.

One voice, that is, except one. That came, as always, exactly one beat behind the others. And, as always, was greeted by coughs, squirms and giggles from the rest of the class.

"Good morning, Miss Witch."

And, as always, she ignored the giggles. And the shortening of her name. She had no intention of letting the children know that she knew they – and

from Good Witch to Bad Witch with a twitch of her eyebrows or a tightening of her lips. It worked with the seven year olds in Jupiter Class at least.

But in her private life? That was another matter entirely. Tamara was crippled with shyness and usually came across either as a complete airhead or an intellectual snob. Whereas the reality was, she was neither of those things.

Tamara loved teaching. She loved the excitement on young faces when they finally "got it" and revelled in the knowledge that she'd put that look there.

It carried her through the endless form filling, the tick box exercises, the countless lesson plans. It also gave her the confidence to stand in front of a group of children and pretend to be something she was not: Confident. Capable. In control.

"That you, of all people, should choose

She loved teaching, loved the excitement on their faces that she had put there

one in particular – called her Miss Witch behind her back.

Perhaps when she'd been doing her teacher training Tamara should have foreseen this scenario and changed her surname to Smith or something similar.

The truth was, she actually quite liked it and found it amazingly useful to switch

to become a teacher, Tam," her sister Amy teased her the day she graduated. "You hated every minute of school."

That was not strictly true. Tamara had loved discovering new (to her) authors and the quiet of the school library. She'd loved daydreaming and writing essays and poetry. ➜

However it was true she'd hated most of the rest of it, particularly when it came to answering questions (she never volunteered) or having to read her work out loud to the rest of the class. As for hanging around at the back of the sports hall while teams were being picked and always, always, always being the last to be chosen, that particular memory still had the power to make her squirm.

Yet now when she stood in front of a classroom full of children, she wasn't uncoordinated, tongue-tied Tamara Wytchford any more. She was either Miss Good Witch or Miss Bad Witch. And she didn't mind which.

He'd never liked school as a kid, hated being stuck indoors when he could be outside, climbing trees or watching wildlife. Perhaps, he thought wryly, if he'd worked harder at school, he'd be able to understand those words on the posters.

He jumped up when he heard his name called, almost knocking over the small chair as he did so. He took a deep breath and walked to Miss Wytchford's desk.

She frowned as he approached. Not a good sign.

"You're here on your own, Mr Martin." Her voice was soft, but clipped. Her eyes cool and grey. "I was hoping to see both you and your wife this evening."

She was either Miss Good Witch or Miss Bad Witch, and she didn't mind which!

Tamara lived for her job and had finally found her niche in life. Her perfect job. Except for one thing...

Parents' evenings.

This evening's promised to be particularly challenging, because this evening she was going to have to face William Martin's parents – and they weren't going to like what she had to say.

Her problem was, when it came to dealing with adults, and parents in particular, Tamara had no Good Witch, Bad Witch to hide behind.

Tom Martin sat carefully on the chair that was several sizes too small for him and waited anxiously for his name to be called. He glanced around the school hall, decorated with model dinosaurs made out of egg cartons and brightly coloured posters filled with words he'd never even heard of.

He took out his phone, looked down at it and wished himself anywhere in the world than where he was now.

So was I, Tom thought bleakly and glanced down at his phone again.

Not that he was really looking at it. He just didn't want to look into those cool, grey eyes. Didn't want her to see the word "loser", as if it was stamped on his forehead for all the world to see.

"We're, um... We're not... She couldn't make it," he mumbled.

Miss Wytchford looked down at the folder on the desk in front of her and her frown deepened. She was about the same age as him, he guessed, but, jeez, she scared the living daylights out of him!

No wonder William called her Miss Witch. Not that Tom encouraged that sort of disrespect, of course, and always pulled him up on it. But, even so...

"Honestly, Tom. You're pathetic." Emma's scathing tone burned deep in his brain. "I don't know why I married you, I really don't. I want a man, not a mouse!"

So that was what she'd done. Exchanged this mouse for a real man who was going places, not stuck in the

BEST IN CLASS

mud like him. Literally, for Tom was a landscape gardener, more at home in worn jeans and muddy boots than sharp, trendy clothes.

He loved his job but was pretty hopeless when it came to chasing up people who owed him money.

Particularly poor old Mrs James. He could never bring himself to charge her anywhere near the going rate for the upkeep of her late husband's beloved garden, and as often as not she forgot to pay him at all.

Mrs James was the final straw for Emma and she'd stormed off, into the arms of her boss, Max. The going places man with the sharp suits and flash car, who owned a string of hair salons, including the one Emma worked in. Max was looking to expand overseas and wanted Emma to go with him.

So she'd done just that, promising to send for William once she was settled, leaving Tom to pick up the pieces of their broken little boy who couldn't understand where Mummy had gone.

Not only broken but angry. William blamed Tom for stopping him going with his Mummy, when the truth was Emma had packed her bags and left them both with barely a backward glance.

Not that he would ever tell William that, of course.

So here he was now, being summoned to the school to "have a little chat about William" with his teacher.

When he'd been at school himself, Tom had been awkward and shy and more than a little terrified at the prospect of "having a little chat" with the teacher. That feeling hadn't lessened any since becoming an adult.

"Mr Martin?" Miss Wytchford's crisp voice cut into his bleak thoughts. "I ➔

asked you and your wife to come here tonight because… Well, because there's been some bullying in the school playground. Nothing serious, of course, but we have a zero tolerance policy in the school and –"

Tom's head shot up. The palms of his large capable hands felt sweaty on his knees. Bullying? Here, in this school?

He knew all about bullying. He had been a victim of it himself more times than he cared to count. Coming to this school brought back so many painful memories. Even back then, the kids had called him "mouse", among other things. It seemed that Emma hadn't been so far off after all.

Now this… this Miss Witch thought he was going to sit there, like a scared little mouse, while some kid did the same thing to William that had been done to him?

Over his dead body!

"Nothing serious?" he repeated, his desire to protect his son overriding his self consciousness. "So you think there is any such thing as 'non serious' bullying? All bullying is serious, Miss Witch."

Half an hour earlier, he'd have been horrified at such a slip of the tongue and it would have completely thrown him. But not now, because this wasn't about him. This was about William. There was no way he was going to stand by while William was the victim of bullying, however "non serious".

"I'm sorry," he went on quickly, as he could see she was about to interrupt. "Bullying is despicable. There's never any excuse for it and I demand it is dealt with immediately."

Just for a fleeting second, he thought he saw something flicker in her eyes, something he recognised. If he didn't know better, he'd think he'd just seen a flicker of fear in those cool, grey eyes.

Tamara looked down at her notes, while she struggled to hold herself together. Mr Martin looked furious. As if at any moment he was going to leap out of his chair and start shouting at her.

This was her first parents' evening and

she'd been warned by more experienced members of staff that certain parents would try to browbeat her.

She felt the familiar fluttering of panic and looked quickly around the room, ready to push her chair back and go and find her head of year who had earlier offered to deal with Mr Martin on her behalf if necessary.

Then she thought of William and her courage returned. Her moment of panic was over.

She drew a deep, steadying breath.

"I'm sorry, Mr Martin. And, obviously we are of one mind in our dislike of bullying, and a commitment to stamping it out before it becomes a problem. But

face. On the one hand, he looked as if he wanted to tell her to mind her own business, but on the other…

Tom Martin looked up at the display of the solar system in the school hall as he waited his turn to see William's teacher. He'd sat in this very same seat, six months earlier. He was sure it had got smaller in that time.

But what a difference that six months had made.

As soon as he found the courage to tell Miss Wychford about Emma leaving him and William, things had changed.

She'd made him see that William's poor behaviour was almost definitely

She had a brief moment of satisfaction when she saw his indignation shrivel

I'm afraid you've got it wrong, Mr Martin. William is not being bullied. He's the one doing the bullying."

She had a brief moment of satisfaction as she saw his anger and indignation shrivel like a leaking balloon. Then she saw something in his eyes that she recognised. She flinched before gathering her courage to continue.

"Has something happened at home?" she asked gently. "I'm not asking to pry into your private life, but we've noticed such a change in William over this last term. When I first met him at the beginning of the school year he was a delightful little boy. Very kind and cooperative. Whereas now…" She chose her words with care. "Well, now he just seems to be angry with everyone and everything. When he's at school, he's a very unhappy, angry little boy. Have you seen any change in his behaviour at home, Mr Martin?"

She saw the struggle on the man's

down to his inability to cope with the changes at home. So Tom had gone away that evening and thought about this very carefully. Then he'd picked up the phone and spoken to his wife. He'd explained that this situation could not be allowed to continue, that William needed to know where he stood.

There was a pause. A very long pause. At one time, Tom would have rushed to fill the silence, desperate to stop her saying the words he'd dreaded to hear.

But this time, he waited.

"I'm not coming back, Tom," Emma said. "Not ever. I want a divorce. Max and I have plans."

"And where does William fit in with these plans?" he asked, struggling to keep his voice level.

Another pause. "I love William to the moon and back. You know I do, Tom," she said quickly. "But you know how important my career is to me, too. I should never have had children. I'm ➜

really not the maternal type. I should never have let you talk me into it."

Tom could have pointed out that Emma had never in her life let anyone talk her into doing something she didn't want to do, least of all him. But, being the mouse he was, he let it go.

"Are you coming home so that we can tell him together?" he asked. "I think it would be better for him."

"Oh no," she said quickly. "I don't think so."

Tom had the same rush of anger he'd felt when he thought William was being bullied. The same fierce desire to do the right thing for his son that overrode his normal diffidence.

"It would be better for him," he said firmly. "And the sooner the better."

To his amazement, she agreed. Just like that, no arguements

certainly looking forward to seeing more of him, since he'd so kindly volunteered to oversee the creation of the school's new kitchen garden which the children were all so excited about.

She was also looking forward to showing him the change in William's work this term and how well he's been doing since he moved up not one but two reading groups recently.

William was, once again, the delightful, eager to learn little boy she'd first known. He'd spoken up really well last week when he'd told the class about his half term visit to see his mother in Spain and how he'd learned to say 'Please can I have some more?' in Spanish.

Of course, his maths still needed work as it was not William's favourite subject and she'd made a note to ask Mr Martin to encourage William to work as hard on

William was once again the delightful, eager to learn little boy he used to be

William had taken it surprisingly well, especially when he realised he could spend summer holidays with his mother in Spain.

"Mr Martin?"

Tom was jerked back to the present at the sound of his name. Miss Wytchford looked up as he approached. Then she smiled at him. It was a very pretty smile, he realised, and it went so well with her warm, grey eyes.

Tamara smiled as Tom Martin approached her desk. He looked very different from the tense, angry man she'd first met, six months earlier. She was

the subjects he wasn't so keen on as on those he enjoyed.

"Good evening, Mr Martin," she said.

"Good evening, Miss Wytchford," he said. Did she imagine it, or was there a little pause between the two syllables of her name? Certainly his smile had the same impish quality as that of his son.

She smiled back. She didn't need to hide behind Miss Good Witch or Bad Witch any more. She was happy being herself now. And one day, who knows, she just might ask Tom Martin to call her Tamara. **MW**

. . . .

FIND MORE STORIES

In My Weekly Specials, out every month, full of good reading for you to enjoy

FANCY THAT!

Fascinating facts on Wine!

◆ Wine glasses should be held by the stem so that the hand does not affect the temperature of the wine.

◆ Toasting started in ancient Rome when they would drop a piece of toasted bread into the wine glass to absorb any unwanted tastes.

◆ Oenophobia is a hatred of wine... yes, it IS a thing.

◆ Soy sauce has 10 times more antioxidants than red wine – and like wine, the longer it ages, the more nuanced the taste.

◆ Global warming may redefine wine growing in future, as even tiny temperature changes can dramatically change the quality of wine.

◆ The world's oldest person attributed her ripe old age of 122 to a diet of olive oil, port wine and 1kg of chocolate every week!

◆ One bottle of wine contains about 2.8lbs of grapes.

◆ Wine-flavoured KitKats are a thing... although you can only get them in Japan.

◆ Yeast that lives on grape skins produces wine by itself – squeeze some grapes into a jar and keep it warm and it'll turn into a kind of wine. Some people believe this was how wine was first discovered.

◆ Not all wines improve with age – in fact 90% of wines ought to be consumed within a year of production, and only a very few last longer than a decade.

◆ Wine bottles are stored on their sides to prevent the cork from drying out and dropping back inside the bottle.

Red wine lowers your risk of stroke, and lessens the risk of developing Type 2 diabetes by up to 30%

◆ Contrary to popular belief, smelling the cork reveals little about the wine – instead check the date stamp and look for drying, mould, or cracks in the cork.

◆ Staying awake for 17 hours leads to a decrease in performance equal to drinking two glasses of wine.

The Bird Table

Her daughter's ploy to bring widowed Rebecca out of
herself wasn't going to work – not at all...

By Linda Lewis

A bird table was absolutely the
last thing Rebecca wanted as a
house warming gift, but she
didn't say that to her daughter and
son-in-law. "Thank you. How lovely,"
she said instead.

Carol produced a packet of bird food
from her capacious bag.

"Here you are, Mum. Put some food out.
Let's see if anyone comes."

She knew what they were up to. Her
late husband had been a keen gardener and
always remembered to feed the birds.

"They're much better at killing pests than
any spray," he'd say.

They were trying to make her feel
at home, help her recover from losing
Martin. For a while, the three of them stood
watching through the window, but not a
single bird appeared.

One of the main reason she'd moved in the
first place was to escape all the memories.
Besides, plenty of other people fed the birds.
They wouldn't starve.

The robin came the next day. His flight
caught her eye as he made a beeline
for the table. He strutted up and down as
if expecting food to magically appear then
he stopped and looked Rebecca right in the
eye, making the breath catch in her throat.

"Go away, you silly bird. There's no food
today. Or tomorrow either."

The robin came back the next day and
the day after that. Each time, he inspected
the empty table, looked at her, then flew
away. Despite herself, Rebecca found
herself watching out for him.

One day she had beans on toast for
lunch. She'd missed going to the shops
because of bad weather and the bread
was on the verge of stale.

One of the main reasons she'd moved was to escape from all the memories

"It will take a few days for them to get
used to it," Daniel said. "You'll be able to
watch the birds while you eat."

"Like you used to do with Dad," added
Carol gently. "We'll bring more food round
tomorrow."

"There's really no need," Rebecca said
quickly. "I can easily get some myself."

The truth was, she had no intention
of putting food out or eating at the table.

I could put it out for the birds...

When two robins appeared, Rebecca
instinctively knew they were a couple. She
swallowed a pang of envy. After a marriage
that lasted thirty-four years, she wasn't used
to being on her own.

Later, as she filled her supermarket
trolley with her usual staples – bread, milk,
potatoes, chicken thighs and fish for the
freezer – a poster caught her eye. The ➡

store had a special offer on mealworms. *Much loved by garden birds, especially robins.* The price had been heavily discounted to ninety-nine pence a packet.

"I suppose I could feed them for a few weeks. Give the parents a good start," she told herself, adding two packets to her cart.

Early the next morning she put some mealworms on the bird table, together with the crust from her loaf of bread.

As nine o'clock approached, she found herself standing by the dining table, waiting for the robins to appear but there was no sign of them.

I might as well have my breakfast here, she thought. When she came back to the table with her porridge, two sparrows were tucking into the mealworms.

"They're not for you!" she shouted. She only just managed to stop herself running outside and shooing them away. They weren't to know, they were only birds.

Something about one of the sparrows drew her eye. His black chest was so crisp and bright, he reminded her of an elderly gentleman wearing his best bib and tucker.

When they flew away, she felt a pang.

Leaving her porridge, she fetched the bag of mealworms and added some more to the table. She'd only just gone back inside when a robin appeared.

"On your own today?" she said. "What's happened? Is Mrs Robin on the nest?"

She chuckled. Now she was talking to birds. Whatever next? she wondered.

It wasn't that she was watching but she began to notice other birds coming to her garden – starlings, blackbirds, even a pair of stately wood pigeons. It would

seem unkind to stop feeding them.

She mentioned the bird table to the manager of the corner shop when she paid for her newspapers.

"I really enjoy watching the birds," she said.

He smiled. "Me too, only I don't get to do that very often, stuck in here. Why don't you try putting up a peanut feeder? These are good, too." He showed her a rectangular feeder. "You put slabs of suet inside."

Rebecca was tempted but the feeder was on the expensive side.

"Not today, thanks – but I'll give the peanuts a go."

The next time her daughter called round she gave Rebecca one of the square feeders, filled with suet. "Before you say anything, Mum, they were on special offer."

Rebecca laughed. She'd never been good at accepting gifts so couldn't blame her daughter for sounding defensive.

"I was going to say thank you, that's all. Let's put it out and see what happens."

It wasn't long before a bird flew down to investigate.

"Is that a blue tit?"

"I don't think so," Carol replied. "They have blue heads, aren't they?"

Rebecca had no idea. "Martin would have known what it was."

Carol gave her a hug. "You could always find out. Borrow a book from the library next time you're there."

Rebecca forced on a smile.

"I haven't been there for ages. My card's probably expired."

"Then get a new one. It's not difficult."

It might not be difficult for her, thought

Rebecca, but avoiding people was the only way she could cope after losing Martin. He was such a well-known, popular man – everywhere she went, people knew him. She started staying at home as much as possible, but that didn't make things any easier.

The garden had been Martin's pride and joy. Every time she cut the grass or trimmed the hedges, she felt like an interloper. After he died, she couldn't get over the feeling that it was *his* garden and that she couldn't change anything. Trying to keep up with all the mowing the pruning and weeding had taken over her life.

Deciding to move had been hard, but she was glad she'd finally done it. Her new home had a smaller, much easier to manage garden. No bird table. It was a lot closer to the train station, too.

The next day, three robins appeared – two adults plus a juvenile. The youngster was so fluffy it looked bigger than its

fixed up." The girl took a few details and quickly produced a brand new card. "If you need any help, just come to the desk."

"Actually, there is something else," Rebecca said. "I'm looking for a book on garden birds…"

"Did you find what you wanted?" the girl asked a few minutes later.

"Yes, I did. Thank you." Rebecca showed her the book she'd chosen. It was crammed with photos and drawings of all the birds that might come to a British garden. "So remind me, how do I go about taking this out?"

The girl took her through the process, then pointed to a poster. "If you like birds, you might be interested in this. A walk in Gladesham Woods, identifying birds by their calls. It's being led by the man who wrote the book you just borrowed – Peter Myers." She gave Rebecca a leaflet. "It's free – and

They fell out when Peter corrected Martin over mistaking a bullfinch for a chaffinch

parents. Once they'd had their fill they flew away. Instantly, five other birds with long tails took their place. She'd seen them before but couldn't remember what they were called.

Her daughter's words came back to her. *Get a book from the library. It's easy.*

The library had changed dramatically since her last visit. She couldn't even find the issue desk.

As panic rose, she heard a friendly voice.

"Can I help? Only you look a bit lost."

The girl couldn't have been more than seventeen. "I've moved house," Rebecca explained. She took her library card from her purse. "I'm not sure this still works."

"Come with me. We'll soon get you

you don't even have to book in advance."

Rebecca thanked her but had no intention of going on the walk.

Peter Myers was the nearest thing their small town had to a local celebrity and was often on the radio, talking about wildlife. He'd belonged to the same gardening club as her late husband. They'd fallen out when Peter had corrected him when he'd mistaken a female bullfinch for a chaffinch.

"Who does he think he is?" Martin had complained when he got home.

After that, if Peter was on the radio, Martin would change the channel. Going on the walk would have felt like a betrayal.

On the bus home, she looked through the book. The first section was titled *How to attract birds to your garden.* Top of ➤

the list was a bird table. Item number two was a bird bath.

A host of memories forced their way into her mind. In her old garden, they'd had a large concrete dish shaped like a shell, which the birds used to bathe in. She and Martin had spent many happy hours watching them but the dish was so heavy, she hadn't even considered taking it with her when she moved.

She called her son. "I'm after getting a bird bath. Could you find one for me?"

It was a huge success. Sometimes several birds would drink peaceably together, at

"A female siskin." Rebecca smiled triumphantly. Before, she would have dismissed it as a greenfinch. They were very similar until you knew what to look for.

It was funny how one day could change an entire life. In the end she'd gone on the bird walk because there was nothing on TV that night. Martin wouldn't have wanted her to stay at home watching repeats if there was something else on offer.

She'd taken to Peter immediately. With his friendly manner and bright eyes, he reminded her of a robin.

Together they watched a pair of sparrows fighting

"I'm after getting a bird bath. Could you find one for me?" she asked her son

other times, squabbles would break out, or a queue would form on the fence as birds waited to take a dip – but the highlight for Rebecca was watching the blackbirds take a bath. They really went for it, sending water flying everywhere.

In fact they were so entertaining, Rebecca started eating her meals at the table rather than from a tray in front of the TV. It really was much nicer.

One day, Rebecca spotted a bird she recognised. It was the male robin who'd first come to the bird table all those months ago, ready to start the process of raising a family, all over again.

Moments later, another bird landed on the peanut feeder.

"Do you know what kind of bird that is?" Peter asked.

over the last scrap of bread, while two coal tits balanced from one of the feeders.

She hadn't wanted the bird table when her family had given it to her. It had been too painful a reminder of what she'd lost – but it had turned out to be the best present she'd ever had.

She smiled as Peter took her hand. Not only had it helped her to fall in love with garden birds once more – it had helped her find love again too. **MW**

•••

THE FIRST BOOK I READ...

Gerald Durrell's books were my favourites, especially *My Family And Other Animals*. I can't remember how old I was when I first encountered them.

Brain Boosters

Missing Link

The answer to each clue is a word which has a link with each of the three words listed.
This word may come at the end (eg **HEAD** linked with **BEACH**, **BIG**, **HAMMER**), at the beginning (eg **BLACK** linked with **BEAUTY**, **BOARD** and **JACK**) or a mixture of the two (eg **STONE** linked with **HAIL**, **LIME** and **WALL**).

ACROSS

2 Bearer, Blow, Light (5)
7 Fine, In, Less (4)
8 Arrow, Cause, Square (4)
9 Collar, Hang, Hot (3)
10 Congestion, Cover, Nurse (6)
11 Immersion, Storage, Water (6)
13 Queen, Tale, Tooth (5)
14 Church, Football, National (6)
16 Hormone, Ring, Under (6)
18 Storm, Teaser, Wash (5)
21 Audio, Copy, Shorthand (6)
23 Acute, Foreign, Local (6)
25 Cotton, Pink, Rummy (3)
26 Decision, Nappy, Nettle (4)
27 Cap, First, Going (4)
28 Hard, Pug, Toffee (5)

DOWN

1 Money, Puppies, Up (4)
2 Holy, Stricken, Tactics (6)
3 Dispatch, Joy, Out (5)
4 Code, Man, Super (7)
5 Chimney, Plate, Stroke (6)
6 China, Idle, Marrow (4)
12 Baths, Holiday, Numerals (5)
13 Back, Cock, Pillow (5)
15 Cartridge, Ride, Wedding (7)
17 Bantam, Fly, Training (6)
19 Breaking, Criminal, Player (6)
20 Healing, Idle, Shake (5)
22 Book, Calendar, Leap (4)
24 Bank, Pad, Worthy (4)

Turn To Page 165 For Solutions

Hidden word in the shaded squares: _____

Just Good Friends

Jim and Linda had known each other forever. Now they were both widowed. But nothing would change

By Fran Tracey

I t was tricky, Jim thought, *not* to iron creases into trousers when you'd had it drummed into you by an army sergeant that they should able to cut through butter.

"I think it looks a bit silly," Linda had said, "a crease in jeans. It doesn't help my cool-gran vibe. Don't take it the wrong way, Jim."

"Of course I won't," Jim replied. "I'll try and remember next time."

Mind you, it was hard to forget instructions from way back – but all too easy to forget current stuff.

He liked ironing for Linda. It was the kind of thing friends did for one another, wasn't it?

"It's a waste of life," she'd told him after he'd winced at the sight of her crumpled blouse when they'd met for coffee a few weeks ago.

"Oh, I enjoy it," he'd replied. "I get all Zen about it."

Linda had been gazing out of the window while he spoke.

Had he been boring her?

"I tell you what," she'd said after a few moments. "How about you do my ironing, I do your pruning? Then your flowers won't get hacked down and your weeds lovingly tended to."

Jim had laughed. He hated gardening. Unlike his wife, Hilary, who had loved the colour that bloomed all year round.

"Hilary will be proud as anything as she gazes down at her roses."

That made Jim smile too.

"It's a deal," he'd said. "I'll collect your ironing tomorrow."

"How about I bring it round to you, with my secateurs?" Linda had said.

And so the arrangement began.

Jim and Linda had known each other for nearly forty years. They'd worked together in a busy office, back in the day.

Jim and his family had moved to live in the same town when their kids were small. When their respective other halves had still been around, they'd socialised together. The odd dinner date, a country walk with their kids. Even one rather interesting camping trip.

"We'll have a camp fire and a singalong," Linda had suggested.

"The kids will love collecting supplies from the site shop, taking some responsibility." Jim warmed to the idea.

"It'll be great fun," they said in unison, laughing together until their manager looked ready to reprimand them.

It turned out there was a gap between dreams and reality where the camping weekend was concerned.

Linda's husband, Barry, had complained about the cold and damp. Admittedly the forecast had changed ➔

and there was a downpour or four. Their tents leaked, despite Linda's frantic attempts to patch them up.

"And this is supposed to be fun?" Barry had protested.

"Apparently so." Jim's wife Hilary had rolled her eyes.

"I'm off to collect firewood," Jim had told the group huddled around a dwindling fire, avoiding his wife's arched-eyebrow look.

The kids had enjoyed buying sweets instead of milk. "So much for responsibility," Barry said.

They didn't repeat the camping trip. Linda and Jim did go away with a group on a charity cycling trip in France, organised through work, which they enjoyed so much they joined the local cycling club.

Their other halves, not natural cyclists, were both happy with the arrangement.

"I'll book a fishing trip later in the year," Barry had said.

"A nice little break learning how to paint with watercolours – that's my dream," Hilary had said.

Jim and Linda studiously ignored the ribbing at work when their cycling club organised a long weekend away the following year, knowing full well it was possible for a man and woman to have a purely platonic relationship.

Because Jim and Linda were friends. Nothing more.

"Our other halves trust us," Jim had said to the jokers.

"He's not my type," Linda had protested.

"We're just good friends," they said. And it was true.

The cycling holiday had been fun, and it had been good to go together.

Jim was shy, Linda bubbly. Had he been on his own he might not have spoken all weekend. Being with Linda meant that wasn't the case.

They went again, every year or so.

Now Barry and Hilary were gone. Barry had passed away five years ago.

"Who'd have thought I'd have missed Mr Grumpy so much?" Linda said over coffee one day.

Jim gave her a reassuring hug, knowing how close she and Barry had been, despite her calling him Mr Grumpy. He knew exactly how it felt to lose someone you loved. His wife had passed away two years before Barry.

"Grief's like waves," Jim said. "Always there, often gentle, but it can floor you, like when the wind whips the sea up and waves crash onto the beach. One thing's for sure, it never goes away."

"Good description," Linda agreed. "My Barry loved the sea."

They'd talk like this over coffee and a cake, but have a laugh too.

"Remember when you were swinging round in the boss's chair and he came in and caught you?"

"And when I stood up I was that dizzy I stumbled and knocked all that paperwork onto the floor," Linda grinned.

"You redeemed yourself by finding that unpaid invoice amongst the mess…"

It was nice for them to reminisce, Jim thought. There was something very comforting about his friendship with Linda. There was a lot to be said for having known someone for eons. And seeing each other helped combat the loneliness they both felt from time to time.

Both had grandchildren, but their families didn't live locally.

On Jim's granddaughter's last visit she had an announcement.

"Here's your invite to my engagement party, Grandad," she said.

Jim wasn't a lover of parties, but he

could hardly turn down an invite to this one, could he? And her young man was just right for her. Everyone should have someone special, shouldn't they? He was delighted for them.

"I'd love to. I hope you're as happy together as I and your Nanna were."

"I hope so too, Grandad," she smiled.

Jim would have to psych himself up

Very lovely.

And it dawned on him that after all these years of friendship something more romantic was developing, a slow-burn kind of love, that arose from the comfort of knowing someone really well, from sharing laughter, grief and ironing.

Was it possible she might feel the same?

"If I agree to Italy, will you be my 'plus

Now something more romantic was developing, a slow-burn kind of love

for the party. There'd be loads of people there. Did you wear a suit? Or trousers and a shirt? He didn't have a clue.

It all felt very daunting.

I'm thinking of going away," Linda said when she dropped off her ironing and tidied up in the garden the following day. His heart flipped. Not for good, he hoped, surprised how much that thought hurt.

"To Italy," she continued.

Jim knew Linda loved Italy. One of her daughters lived there.

She pushed a holiday brochure across the table. Phew. He could breathe again.

"Camping. Fancy joining me? Thought we could hire bikes, cycle around the countryside. Take it easy, of course, what with our knees and hips and all that. Be like the good old days – only with more stops and lots of embrocation."

He flicked through the brochure. She'd marked a page. The campsite looked nice. You didn't have to put up your own tent, which was a bonus.

Jim looked up. She was smiling.

"If I say yes it will be on one condition."

They were sitting in the garden, admiring her work on the roses. Linda's cheeks were pink, her hair windswept and she had a smudge of dirt on her nose, but she looked lovely, he thought.

one' at the engagement do?" Jim pushed the invitation across the table.

"How lovely." Linda smiled. "An engagement. I do love a party. If you'll iron my dress?"

"It's a deal," he smiled, leaning over, brushing the dirt from her nose and kissing her lightly on the cheek.

"It's good to have a friend with benefits," he smiled.

A breeze ruffled the roses and a soft pink petal dropped into Jim's lap. Hilary looking down and smiling on them, he thought, happy for them.

The next time he kissed Linda it was on the lips.

"That was nice," she said, resting her head on his shoulder. They stayed there a while, comfortable as anything.

Maybe it wouldn't be too long before they were issuing invitations to their own engagement party, Jim thought – and then Linda could be his plus one for the rest of their lives. **MW**

....

THE FIRST BOOK I READ...

The first novels I clearly remember are the *Mallory Towers* books by Enid Blyton. I so envied apple-pie beds, midnight feasts and anchovy paste sandwiches. I suspect the reality was rather different!

Spellbound!

The unassuming Great Geraldo certainly turns
out to have some surprises up his sleeve...

By Jean Buchanan

Tim Carter always liked birthday parties, especially his own. He was looking forward to his ninth birthday party, to be held in the garden if the early summer weather held.

He and his mother had settled the date (easy, his birthday fell on a Saturday) and made a shopping list. Then came the important question of the entertainment.

All of Tim's friends' parties featured professional entertainers. Naturally he wanted to have the current favourite, Spiky Mikey, a young man with wild hair who did juggling, unicycling and things with budgerigars.

option, and well known to be the pits.

Then Tim and his mother compiled the guest list, and a blot appeared on Tim's horizon. That blot was Jeremy Jones, the class bully, who demanded an invitation the moment he heard about The Great Geraldo. Jeremy fancied himself as a conjuror, having been given the largest magic set on the market, and he practised with astonishing application.

To make things worse, Tim had been to Jeremy's recent birthday party, and so – his mother told him – he owed Jeremy an invitation.

There was no escape. Tim just hoped that his father would be able to keep Jeremy in order.

Tim reasoned he had to be better than Uncle Chucklebun, known to be the pits

But Spiky Mikey was booked solid for months, so they had to settle for an unknown quantity, The Great Geraldo ("magic tricks for all the family"), who advertised in their newsagent's window at, Tim's mother was pleased to note, half the fee of Spiky Mikey.

Tim reckoned that The Great Geraldo couldn't be all that great if he advertised on scruffy postcards in shop windows, but he had to be better than Uncle Chucklebun, who was the only other

When the great day arrived, the weather was brilliant, tooling up for a perfect afternoon. The sun shone, the birds were sang, and a gentle breeze played around the climbing roses.

Then Tim's father announced that he had to go to work after all, as one of his colleagues was ill, and they needed a full workforce to sell sofas. He quickly put tables and chairs out on the patio, and left Tim and his mother to get on with the other preparations. ➡

They were just finishing their lunch when the doorbell rang.

It was Jeremy, half an hour early, accompanied by his rather embarrassed mother. He burst in and rushed through the house into the garden shouting, "Where is he? Where's the conjuror? I bet I'm miles better than him!"

"I'm so sorry," said Jeremy's mother. "He was very keen to get here. He's really looking forward to it."

Tim's mother bit her lip and invited Mrs Jones in, but she declined, claiming that this was a really good chance for her to do a big supermarket shop.

"Jeremy really hates coming with me. I'll be back to pick him up."

"Come as early as you like," said Tim's mother. She waved Mrs Jones off regretfully as her large Volvo trundled away, and was just on her way inside when a voice hailed her.

"Mrs Carter?"

She turned round. An elderly man with untidy white hair was coming up the path. He wore a blue collarless shirt and old corduroy trousers held up with string. He was carrying a battered suitcase.

"Good afternoon, dear madam." He shook her hand warmly. "I am Geraldo. The Great Geraldo. At your service."

"Oh, yes, of course. The entertainer."

"Exactly."

He followed her into the house. Probably a retired actor, she thought, trying not to seem disappointed. He wasn't quite as she'd envisaged The Great Geraldo when they'd spoken on the phone. Maybe his costume was in the suitcase.

"Now, I expect you need to change, or get ready, but how about a cup of tea first?"

"Refreshment would be most welcome, dear lady. The exercise of prestidigitation, or magic, demands great concentration of the physical and mental powers. A slice of pie would be nice."

She sat him in the dining room with mixed salad, a slice of quiche, and brown bread and butter, followed by strawberry ice cream and a cup of tea. Then he said he would rest on the sofa for ten minutes or so. "My pre-performance meditation, dear lady. It assists the creative process."

She noticed a small glass of brandy on the table, and made a mental note to lock the drinks cupboard.

Meanwhile Tim, who had been chased all round the garden several times by Jeremy, was feeling hot, sticky and distinctly unbirthdayish, but cheered up when the rest of his guests arrived on time and on their best behaviour, waving cards and presents. They sat down on tartan rugs on the grass to await the performance.

Jeremy Jones, at the far end of the garden, stopped throwing earth over the fence at next door's dog, charged through the herb bed and then squeezed himself into the front row. The Great Geraldo emerged from the house, still in his old shirt and trousers, lugging his suitcase.

There was polite applause. He took up a position midway between the apple-tree and the shed.

"Tell me, children," he began. "What does a magician need?"

"A magic set!" shouted Jeremy.

"Anything else?" asked Geraldo.

Suggestions came thick and fast. A robe! A hat! A magic wand! A cloak! A magic bag!

"All very good ideas," said Geraldo approvingly. "And here I have…" He opened his suitcase, and two doves flew out and perched in the apple tree.

"He had them up his sleeve," said Jeremy smugly.

only a costume. I expect he hired it."

Geraldo reached into his case and brought out a black velvet bag. He turned it inside out to show that it was empty, and then from it he produced, in rapid succession, a pint of milk ("I don't know what that's doing in there."), a string of silk handkerchiefs, a bunch of paper flowers, and a pencil-case, which he presented to Tim.

"They were all hidden up his sleeve," snorted Jeremy.

"Pretty big sleeve," said Tim.

Geraldo ignored both of them and continued serenely. He borrowed a guest's shoe, wrapped it in an old newspaper and hurled it into the air.

There was a flash and a puff of smoke, the newspaper disappeared, and blue

He produced a pint of milk – "I don't know what that's doing in there…"

Geraldo reached into the case. "My magic robe." He held it up – it was made of deep purple silky material that shimmered in the sunlight. He shook out the creases.

"I've got a dressing-gown that's better than that," scoffed Jeremy.

Geraldo ignored him, and put the long robe on carefully, fixing it at the neck and waist. He looked taller. He reached into his suitcase again and produced a pointy hat surmounted by a silver crescent moon. He put it on, and it pushed his straggly white hair into some sort of order on his collar.

"Now do I look the part?" he asked.

"Yes! Yes!" cried all the children except for Jeremy, who remarked loudly, "It's

ribbons floated down to the ground.

"I've got a book that tells you how to do that," said Jeremy.

"What about my shoe?" came a shout from the audience.

Geraldo smiled reassuringly and produced it from behind the owner's back. Then he reached into his suitcase and brought out a dozen shiny metal hoops which he threw up into the air one by one, and they came down in a glittering silvery chain, all linked together.

"I can do that," muttered Jeremy. "Well, nearly."

Geraldo borrowed a watch, turned it into a white rabbit, then back into a watch. He borrowed a pair of sunglasses ➡

and turned them into a pair of goldfish in a tinted glass bowl ("I always think this one is rather witty"), then he turned them back into a pair of sunglasses, despite the owner's assertions that he would rather have the fish. Jeremy sniggered and pointed knowingly to his sleeve.

The act proceeded with loudly-whispered comments and sometimes even advice from Jeremy, but Geraldo ignored him and continued unruffled.

"For my last trick," he said eventually, "I shall require the assistance of someone who knows a bit about magic."

"Me! Me!" shouted Jeremy.

"Very good, young sir," said Geraldo. "Come here and stand next to me."

Jeremy leaped up and rushed forward.

"You will need a junior magician's robe, of course," said Geraldo. He rummaged in his suitcase, brought out a smaller star-spangled robe, and helped

"Do you do shoplifting?" Jeremy asked brightly.

"I generally find shops rather heavy," said Geraldo smoothly, just as Tim's mother returned with the shoebox. "Thank you so much, dear lady. Perhaps your son would bring it to me."

Tim fetched the shoebox and Geraldo said, "Hold on to it for a moment." Then he turned to Jeremy, who was still smirking, his arms full of the table-tennis bat, the carton of eggs and the hamster, which had fallen asleep.

"Now for my last trick," said Geraldo, "I expect you all wondered whether I'd got one of these, and this time it really is up my sleeve." He extracted a long, slim wand from his sleeve and held it up in the air. "We must all concentrate," he said. "Especially you," he added to Jeremy. "Concentrate, and think… Magic!"

There was a blinding flash followed by

Tim's mother turned white, picked up the shoebox and went to speak to her

Jeremy into it. Jeremy promptly patted up and down each arm.

"There's nothing up the sleeves," said Geraldo. "And you'll need a hat as well." He produced one from thin air. Jeremy grabbed it and jammed it on his head.

"Now you look the part," said Geraldo. "A round of applause for my assistant!" There were a few slow handclaps, a few boos, and a small ripple of laughter.

"We shall need a cardboard box, of modest size. Maybe a shoebox. Perhaps Madam would oblige?" Geraldo looked at Tim's mother, who went inside to get the box from Tim's new trainers.

Geraldo casually produced a table-tennis bat and a hamster from Jeremy's left ear, and then half-a-dozen eggs from his right ear.

a spray of purple and silver stars. Jeremy disappeared, leaving behind his junior magician's robe and hat which collapsed into a crumpled heap. There was no sign, either, of the table-tennis bat, the hamster, or the carton of eggs.

A few children tittered nervously and looked around, clearly expecting Jeremy to emerge from the shed.

Geraldo seemed unconcerned. He bent down and picked up the hat and the junior magician's robe. "Why, there you are," he said to a small greenish-brown frog which was glaring up him. He put the robe and hat carefully back into his suitcase, then picked up the frog, which croaked mournfully at him. He took the shoebox from Tim and popped the frog inside.

"Yes, I was sure that would come in

useful," he said, as he replaced the lid.

The he bowed. "Thank you, boys and girls. You have been a most appreciative audience. The performance is at an end."

There was a smattering of bemused applause. Tim's mother ushered the children to the patio and brought out the food. When she spoke to Geraldo again he was busy loading a paper plate with sausage rolls and crisps.

"You surely don't expect me to believe that you've turned that child into a frog?"

"Not really," said Geraldo briskly, helping himself to some cheese straws.

"Hello!" Jeremy's mother came round the corner of the house into the garden. Tim's mother turned white, picked up the shoebox and went to speak to her.

"I had to do it, you know," said Geraldo quietly to Tim.

"What? Turn him into a frog?"

Geraldo nodded He produced a goblet of dark-red wine from his pocket, drank deeply, and put it back into his pocket.

"Wilful disparagement of my professional abilities," he said. "And anyway, the boy was a pain."

"He was very rude to you," agreed Tim indignantly.

"And he wasn't exactly kind to you. Now where did I put my suitcase? Ah, yes." He finished his crisps, put down his paper plate, and whistled to the two doves which flew down from the apple-tree and settled on his shoulders.

"Time I moved on," he said, shaking Tim's hand. "I'll see myself out. And you'd better tell those good ladies," he added, watching as Tim's mother gingerly handed the shoebox to Jeremy's mother, "that my spells only last for a few days."

"Wow," said Tim.

"A few days," said Geraldo. "Usually." Ⓜ

• •

THE FIRST BOOK I READ...

My first standout novel, which I bought after reading a short, hilarious extract from it in a school textbook when I was about 11, was *The Sword In The Stone* by T. H. White.

A Mouse In The House

Becca was made of sterner stuff, so no way was she going to let a little mouse ruin her plans for a day off

By Florence Moss

Becca threw another pile of tat into the bin and clapped the dust from her hands.

"I need a cuppa," she said aloud, putting the kettle on to reward herself.

A good throw-out though, was its own reward. All those space-hogging books and bits. All those dowdy clothes that were only fit for decorating in. How many decorating outfits did she need?

She sat down amid more piles of tat and put her feet up on the footstool. There was a time when a gas leak at work and an unexpected day off would have had her rushing to town or lunch with her mum. Not today. A day off, with Drew and the kids out, and a chance to blitz their rubbish was its own kind of bliss.

She was enjoying the strange feeling of luxury, dipping a crafty digestive into her tea and thinking about a soak in the bath later when she saw a mouse under the coffee table. Tea splashed onto her arm and her biscuit sank into her mug as she jumped with shock.

"Oh, no!" She sat, terrified and rigid.

Trying to be rational – it was only a small mouse – she told herself that she'd produced two children, she could change tyres and fill skips with rubble with the best of them. She could stand up to her children's head teacher and was no slacker when it came to dealing with tricky customers at work. But a mouse?

She drew her knees up and wondered what to do.

I'll phone Drew she thought, but couldn't see her phone.

The mouse stayed where it was, under the coffee table, doubtlessly aware that it had been spotted.

Looking for a solution her eyes scanned the untidy room and she was relieved to see her phone on the floor by

her chair. Barely breathing she twisted herself around to snatch it up, stretching her fingers slowly so that the mouse couldn't hear her. With her eyes fixed on its furry brown body she snatched the phone up.

"Drew," she whispered. "There's a mouse under the coffee table."

"What d'you want me to do about it?" Noisy construction work in the background didn't hide his amusement.

"Move it!" Becca kept her eyes on the tiny rodent as she spoke. If it moved she wanted to know where it went.

"Becca, you chopped a tree down last week. How can you be scared of a mouse?" He stifled a laugh.

"Mice and trees are different things. Come and get it, Drew."

"I'm fifty miles away," Drew laughed.

"Be like that then!" Becca cut the call and wondered what to do.

Her day had started with the unexpected joy of a day off work, the house to herself and a massive de-clutter. There were still a few hours of bliss and throwing out ahead if only she could get someone to shoo the mouse away. Until she did it was going to sit there, just looking at her.

"Mum," she wailed into her mother's answer machine. "Where are you?"

"Jenny?" she said when her sister's phone went to voicemail. It crossed her mind to phone the children's school and

get her son to come home in a taxi, but she thought better of it.

"I won't be defeated," she told the mouse who seemed to have moved a notch since her last call. "I won't." Her voice wavered.

She thought of the time she dashed an injured neighbor to Casualty and the day she fixed her mum's broken fence. Women like her didn't cower from mice.

With a sudden lunge, Becca dived at the mouse, ready to chase it away.

"What?" The furry thing didn't budge. Becca looked closely and realized she'd been held captive by an outgrown mitten whose partner was in the bin, where it belonged. It looked just like a mouse!

"Did you want me?" her mum asked, returning her call.

"False alarm," Becca said, taking her cup to the kitchen.

"You sounded desperate," her sister said when she too returned her call.

"Did I?" Becca said making her way to the airing cupboard which was full of shabby towels and tat. She had the whole day ahead of her to sort it… Ⓜ

....

THE FIRST BOOK I READ…

My Family and Other Animals by Gerald **Durrell. The Greek landscape, the animals, characters and a mirror held up to the humour and antics of family life… just joyful!**

On The Horizon

Far from being an ending, retirement can open up new opportunities that you never thought were possible…

By Julie Goodall

I appreciate the little party you've got for me, but I hope it's OK to break it up a bit early. We're off for a short drive down to Weymouth."

Francis stared at Darryl for a moment, taken aback. It was unlike her husband to do anything particularly spontaneous, yet his tone seemed to imply that he'd had this planned all along.

She glanced at the grandkids but Darryl, apparently, had read her mind.

"They'll be OK. It's Friday. No school tomorrow. Come on then, guys and gals. Toilet, then into the cars. We've got a few hours before it gets dark."

Francis looked at Janet, astonishment reflected in her daughter's eyes.

"He only retired two hours ago," Janet whispered. "Do you think it's already addled his brain?"

They laughed quietly, then went about getting the three boys galvanised and into the MPV's backseat. It was a seven seater so it was decided it was easier to all go

together, but Darryl insisted he drive.

"I'm insured for any car," he told them, easing the keys from his son-in-law's hand. "I'm retired now, not incapable."

Janet shot a little "O" expression at her mother and the two women climbed into the back, shifting the two oldest boys into the seats by the boot.

Francis settled back, nicely filled with sausage rolls, cake and vol au vents, a frisson of excitement buzzing in her chest. As a mum and then grandma, she'd been used to taking control for longer than she could remember. How refreshing for someone else to take charge for a change.

When they arrived at the seafront, an evening sun glinted brightly on the ocean, seagulls squawking and swooping in hopes of retrieving dropped chips on the promenade.

The car slowed and Francis expected Darryl to turn right towards one of the car parks behind the town, yet he continued on towards the pavilion, looped around

and drove back along the seafront and out past Sealife Centre, heading east. Francis was silently thankful she had changed from her heels to her flats.

"Erm, Darryl? Where are you going? We don't want to have to walk too far. The boys have had a long week…"

"We'll be back. We just have to go somewhere first."

Again, the two women exchanged a look and Francis knew by Darryl's tone that there was no point in asking further.

Freddie and Finlay were practically bouncing with excitement and Mickie, the youngest, pointed at a Golden Retriever jumping up at its owner eating an ice cream. After negotiating some early evening traffic, the MPV slowed and Darryl indicated right.

"It's the caravan park." Janet stated the obvious, her words muffled behind her hand and Francis nodded, bemused. Freddie and Finlay began shouting about going on holiday and Darryl grinned in the rear view mirror. ➡

The view was over the cliffs and out to sea, where a ferry was coming in

"We haven't got any luggage," Janet whispered again, looking at Simon who had turned and raised his eyebrows from the front seat.

"We're only forty minutes from home. Not far to pop back. Wait here," Darryl continued, opening the driver door as he pulled up to Reception. "I won't be long."

By the time the rest of the family had concluded he'd lost his marbles, Darryl was back, holding a key with a large fob. He drove slowly through the caravan park, asking the boys to look out for an area named Wheatcliffe. Finlay saw it first, gave a shout and next they were to look out for caravan number 610. This time it

of a passion and, at times, he had hated it, but he'd continued to bring in a wage while Francis had brought up the children, returned to work in home-based catering and helped regularly with the three boys. Greg and Harry both lived north of London so she and Darryl travelled to visit the rest of the family. Life had always been hectic but she wouldn't have had it any other way.

"Fran?"

Quickly, Francis moved further along the caravan. The kitchen was well-equipped with a microwave, fridge freezer and even a washing machine, but the best thing of

All this and she could have a dog, too? Surely she would wake up any moment!

was Freddie who took the glory and soon they all tumbled out of the car, Mickie released from his seat.

Inside, the caravan was immaculate, gleaming with décor in subtle shades of green and beige. The lounge area was spacious, boasting a good sized TV, dvd player, and an inviting electric fire to heat up cooler nights. It wouldn't be needed today though, Francis reflected, thinking of the evening sun throwing its diamonds onto the English Channel below.

"Come and see the kitchen."

Francis was amused to see a glint of excitement in Darryl's eyes and heard a lift in his voice that she hadn't heard for some time. He'd worked hard ever since they'd been teenagers and when there was no longer much of a call for clockmakers, he'd retrained in IT. It had not been much

all was the view from the kitchen sink…

"Wow! Look at this!"

The view was uninterrupted, over the cliff and out to sea. In the distance, a Condor ferry was making its way back from the Channel Isles, and Francis recalled the times they and the children had sailed across to Guernsey, one of her favourite places in the world.

"It's beautiful."

Francis heard a rustling and turned to her husband of nearly forty years.

"It's yours," he said.

Grinning from ear to ear, Francis took the bouquet from him with a smile.

"What on earth have I done to deserve this? It's you who's just retired…"

Behind them, the three boys were exploring the bedrooms, noisily arguing over who'd have which bed.

Darryl laughed aloud. "Not the flowers, you numpty. The caravan. It's ours. We've bought it."

In the lounge, Janet and Simon stopped in mid-conversation, then continued, pretending they hadn't heard.

Francis turned and stared out at the ferry, disbelief stunning her into silence. A million questions swirled in her head.

For a few moments, Darryl let her be then she felt his hand slip into hers. The front door to the caravan closed quietly and she guessed her daughter and son-in-law had gone outside. The boys were now inspecting the shower room and she heard the ominous sound of taps being turned on.

"How have we bought it?" she asked, turning towards him. She knew they were close to finishing paying off the mortgage, but their combined wage wasn't enough to afford something like this.

Darryl tapped his nose.

"A little life insurance policy payout that I kept to myself. I've been running it since the eighties. It pays out if you don't croak before a certain time period."

"You sneaky…"

Fortunately, Mickie flew past at that moment, yelling for his mum.

"She's outside, sweetheart," Francis said and the three year old banged on the door until Janet came in to rescue him.

Francis took the flowers from Darryl, put the plug in the sink and filled it enough to give the stems a drink.

"I know you've always wanted to live next to the sea, Fran, but I know you also don't feel you can move, what with being there for the boys after school and so on. This way, we've got the best of both worlds, only forty minutes away at most. We can bring the boys down at the weekends if we

want to. It'll give Janet and Simon a rest."

"I just… I can't believe it."

"They let you bring dogs, too."

"Well, we haven't got a…" Francis looked at him sideways. "What do you mean 'they let you bring dogs'?"

"Well, now that I'm no longer at work, I want to work off some of this weight – or you might go off me."

He winked cheekily and led her towards the other end of the caravan to explore the three bedrooms, and shower room where Freddie and Finlay were playing with the taps.

"Oi you two!" Darryl said in his Grandad voice. The boys jumped and fled, leaving them to turn off the taps.

Francis thought that the last time she'd felt this happy was after each grandchild was born. All this and, at last, she could have a dog too? Surely, any moment, she would wake up.

"All I got you was a watch," she grinned sheepishly.

"I don't need anything. Just my family to be happy," Darryl responded and he moved to the back door, unlocked it and opened it wide. The boys were running around like headless chickens and Janet and Simon were by the car, deep in conversation. Francis held Darryl close and looked out over the cliff at the ferry, growing bigger as it headed for port.

"It's perfect," she whispered, her gaze focusing on where the sky meets the sea, knowing she could look at it any time she wanted. Thanks to Darryl, the horizon was in their sights and now there were limits on what lay beyond. Ⓜ

THE FIRST BOOK I READ…

The first novel I remember reading was *The Book of Brownies* when I was seven. My dad died and I read it over twenty times while I escaped into Enid's world.

ILLUSTRATIONS: ISTOCKPHOTO, REX/SHUTTERSTOCK

Circle Of Blue

Life has a way of giving you what you need – although not always in the way you thought you wanted it…

By Della Galton

Bryony was lying on her back on the trampoline. Her heart was pounding as though she'd just run a marathon and sweat poured down her face. She didn't remember trampolining being such hard work! But then the last time she'd been on one she'd probably been aged about 25. Oh, and fit. Neither of which was the case now.

Above her head, outlined within the trampoline's mesh safety surround, was a perfect circle of blue. It was a beautiful day, the hottest Sunday in September and she was spending it at Tim's. He had a much bigger garden than hers at home.

At the moment his border terrier was charging across it at top speed, his gaze also on the sky but for an entirely different reason. Jackson was chasing pigeons for all his little heart was worth. Sometimes,

marathon. Not that she minded. In fact it didn't get any better than this: a sunshine Sunday with Tim pottering somewhere in one of his greenhouses, a dog racing about without a care in the world, and Ellie all to herself. Bliss.

She looked back up at the circle of blue and fleetingly her mind flicked back to another long ago summer…

To another circle, but this one on a pregnancy tester which rested on the edge of the bath, while Bryony waited for a line of blue. Waited in vain. So many testers, so much hope, fading little by little, as first the months and then the years went by.

Summers had been tinged with sadness in those days. She and her husband had lived next door to a park and when the sun came out, so did the children. It had been impossible to go into her garden without hearing the squeals of children splashing in the paddling pool or being

It didn't get any better than this: a sunshine day without a care in the world

Bryony thought they deliberately taunted him by swooping low over his head and then banking upwards again into the eternal blue.

She wished she had half his energy. Ellie, who also had a surplus of energy – mind you, what eleven-year-old didn't? – had just disappeared into the house to fetch a drink. Bryony was making the most of it. When Ellie came back she would be enlisted in another bouncing

pushed by their mums on the swings, or playing tag across the grass.

It had been impossible not to hear mothers scolding their children. Back in those days she had wanted to march across to them and shout, "You don't know how lucky you are. You should be treasuring them. You should be making the most of every precious moment!"

She never did that of course. She wasn't so idealistic that she didn't realise ➡

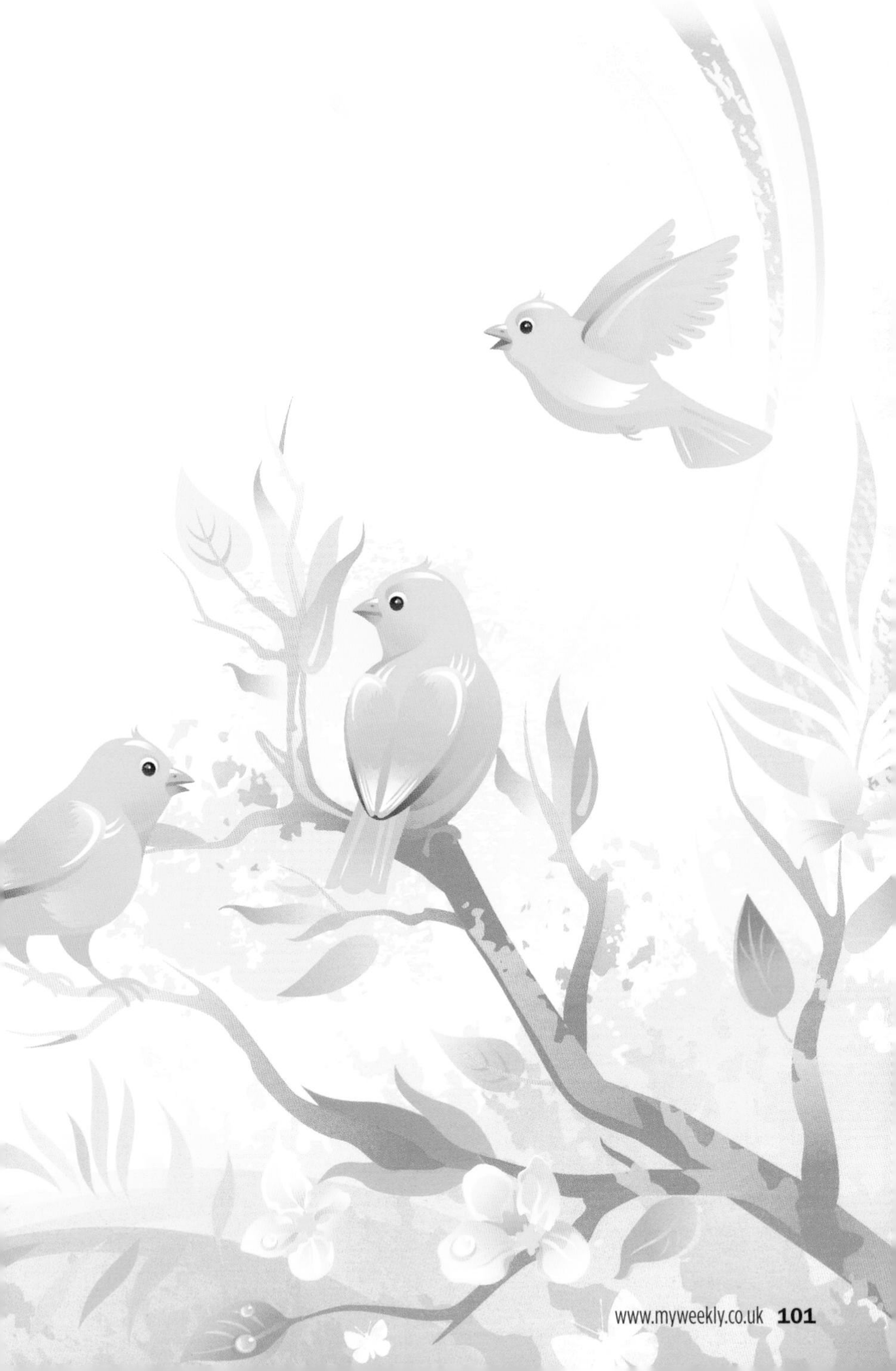

having kids wasn't all picnics in the park and princess parties. She knew it was incredibly hard work. Her sister had twins – Millicent May and Gareth.

"Take one of them on," she used to joke. "Be my guest." And Bryony would always smile and pick one of them up and say, "Right then, cutie pie. Time to come and live with your Auntie B." Then, still smiling, she would put the child back down again and say, "On second thoughts, I think you'd better stay here with your mum." And each time she did it, her heart would break a little more.

Often, her sister would say, "Time you had your own, isn't it?"

And Bryony would nod and pretend that she was nonchalant about the whole thing. "What would I be wanting with babies? I value my freedom too much."

Because she could never bear to share with anyone, not even her closest family, how very hard it was to live in a world where she couldn't have the one thing she'd always wanted the most.

Ellie's voice broke into her musings and Bryony opened her eyes.

"Are you asleep?" Ellie asked.

"Of course not."

"You were snoring." Ellie's eyes narrowed accusingly.

"No way!"

Bryony sat up with her most alert expression fixed in place. Ellie beamed, showing the gap in her front teeth.

"Can we play the game when you have to guess the celebrity and you're only allowed one syllable per bounce?"

"We can," Bryony said, wishing she

hadn't invented it. Still, at least celebrities had short names on the whole. The TV program version had been murder.

When she'd hit forty-three she'd all but given up on having children. She'd been divorced by then.

"I'm sorry," her ex had said one Saturday morning at breakfast, "But I've met someone else."

She had found out later that the someone else was younger, slimmer, and (far more painfully) more fertile than she was. Within a year of them separating her ex had been part of a family, which included children.

Bryony had moved away from the park and tried not to mind. For eighteen months she'd concentrated on her work, which was in personnel and involved matching prospective job applicants to jobs. She was good at it. She had a knack for knowing who would be right for what. Three years after her divorce she had opened her own agency.

That's where she had met Tim. He'd been looking for a job in horticulture. She had found him one.

The attraction between them had been instant and mutual. On their third date he'd presented her with a bunch of bluebells because she had told him blue was her favourite colour. On their sixth date he'd introduced her to his daughter. By then they were finishing each other's sentences.

"Ellie's mum and I split up when she was seven," he'd told her. "But I have Ellie every other weekend, all weekend." His

gaze held hers. "Are you OK with that?"

"I love kids," she'd said and kissed him.

Luckily she and Ellie had got on well from the start.

"Probably because I have a similar mental age to her," Bryony had joked. And so she had become, not mother, not playmate, and certainly not wicked stepmother, but somehow a mixture of the best bits of all three.

The last couple of years had been the happiest of her life. She had shared things with Tim she had never told anyone. And he had reciprocated.

"I lost my parents when I was four," he had said one night. "They died in a car accident on their way back from a long weekend in the Lake District. I was brought up by my ageing grandfather." He paused. "He did his best, but he wasn't

Are you two ready for some lunch?" Tim came across to the trampoline. He had earth on his hands, which he brushed off on his combat trousers. "Whose turn is it to make it anyway?"

"Mine," Bryony said. "There's only so much trampolining an old lady can do."

"You're not old," Ellie said fiercely, shaking her head so hard her plaits swung.

"I knew there was a reason I love you," Bryony told her.

"I'll do dessert," Tim promised.

So after their platter of cheese and olive bread and tomatoes cut in fancy shapes to amuse Ellie he went off to get it.

"Ice cream! Yay!" Ellie squealed as she saw him coming back across the grass with knickerbocker glory glasses.

"Strawberry and vanilla for you, and Chocolate and vanilla for Bryony."

When secrets are brought out into the light they disappear in the morning sun

really that used to kids. In his day it was the woman of the household who did the child rearing. It was OK, but…"

"Not ideal," Bryony said, grabbing his hand and squeezing tight.

Not ideal was the understatement of the year, she suspected, seeing that Tim's eyes were a little glittery.

"I don't talk about this stuff much," he had added gruffly.

However, since then they had talked about lots of stuff – some of it good, some of it sad. They had cried together as well as laughed together.

And Bryony knew that they had both started to heal too, because when secrets are brought out into the light they are very often no more substantial than spider's webs, which might shine brightly in the frost but tend to disappear completely in the morning sun.

He handed them over. Ellie's had a pink wafer in it. Hers had a cocktail umbrella, blue with purple flowers.

When she took it out she saw that it was attached to something by a ribbon.

She pulled it out and it was another little circle of blue. But this one was a ring, inset with diamond and sapphires that glinted in the sun as she turned it over on the palm of her hand.

Tim's gaze met hers. "Would you do me the very great honour…?" he began.

But he didn't need to finish that sentence either… **MW**

On The Run

Our plans were all in place, the RV agreed… but would our getaway be foiled by a traffic tailback?

By Val Bowes

"You can't be optimistic with misty optics," says Reggie, getting busy with the lens-cleaner.

He says it every time he cleans his glasses. He reckons cleaning his glasses helps him think and, as he thinks he's the Napoleon of Crime, he tends to think rather a lot, if you get my drift.

Shoving the specs back on his face, he points at me.

"Wheels. Make sure you don't get none of them Mini things. We want

"Leroy can get them – right, Leroy? Leroy? Leroy!"

Leroy's head nods up and down but even Reg can't kid himself it's in agreement. He reaches out, grabs the wires and yanks the little buds out of Leroy's ears. We don't get the impression that he cares very much how Leroy's ears feel about it.

"Hey!" Leroy snatches his iPhone back. "I was listening to that!"

"Well, get your ears round this. Car keys. Get them. Right?"

"Aw, man! You're not still thinking

"Your grand-pappy's depending on you, son. Don't let him down"

something with capacity. You know?"

It's plain Reggie's planning something rather bigger than the Italian Job.

"Wilco, Boss." I put two fingers to my forehead and flick them as if I'm getting rid of something nasty. They do it in American films. Rather a lot.

Reg apparently decides it's a case of getting into the spirit of the thing, not taking the Mick. I don't disillusion him.

He gets back to being Napoleon. "Car keys. Fingers, your job."

She shakes her head.

"Nothing doing. I'm the first they'd come down on after the last couple of outings. Make Leroy do it."

Reg knows she's right but he pretends to give it some thought, then nods sharply.

of doing this thing? You can't…"

"Your grand-pappy ever use that word?" Reggie isn't about to let his authority be challenged for the second time. "He's for this as much as the rest of us. He's depending on you, son. Don't let him down, you hear what I'm sayin'?"

Leroy rolls his eyes at the rest of us. Then he returns the earpieces to their natural habitat and goes back to nodding his head.

"No mistakes. We're doing it." Reg stares each of us in

the eye, daring us to contradict him. "The Big One. Right. Synchronise watches."

"Not now, Reg. Better do it tomorrow. Just to be on the safe side." Fingers lays her hand on his wrist.

Jack the Cap clears his throat loudly and Ted (Hard-man) Gordon shuffles on his chair and looks daggers, but neither of them dares say anything. Fingers treats them to a raised eyebrow. Then she removes her hand from Reggie's wrist. "Right then." Reg clearly ➡

needs to get back the ascendancy and sticks out his chest.

"Tomorrow. Nobody gets in our way, you hearin' me?"

"Call yourself a driver?"

Yes, Fred. I do. When I'm given the chance to actually drive and not crawl one wheel-turn every five minutes, that is.

"Huh! I'd have been through this lot before you could say knife."

Freddie reckons he used to be Fast Freddie, back in the day. Best getaway driver in the south-east. Yes, well. Taxis to Heathrow earn their corn, given the M25's tendency to resemble a car park, but no one could carve a way through this

"Tipped us off about this, didn't he? Wouldn't have known if he hadn't told us." Reggie relishes any chance to get one over on The Cap. He taps me on the shoulder. "ETA. How long?"

"Piece of string?" I reply tartly.

The insistent two-tones are right behind us now, and we squeeze over to let them pass. But they don't pass. They pull in front of us, blocking the path and forcing us to a stop. I ignore the outbreak of tutting.

"Rozzers!" hisses Reg, as two officers decant from the police car. "What dirty rat split on us?"

"Ma Brown, betcha!" Fingers whispers. "Spoilsport!"

Fingers bats her eyelashes. I can't help feeling she's being a little hopeful here

lot without either a helicopter or a vehicle that breathed in and went sideways.

Even the two-tones sounding behind us for the past few minutes haven't got past. Eventually, whatever was causing the blockage clears a little and we begin to proceed at a more reasonable pace.

"We'll never make it," Jack grumbles. "Should have left earlier. Didn't I say, we should have left earlier?"

He scowls at Ted, who glares and mutters under his breath.

"Not my fault. I wasn't the one who needed to…"

"Now, now, boys," says Fingers. "Play nicely." I glance into my rear-view mirror and catch the wink.

"Plenty of time, mi man," says Delroy. He beams a big melon smile from the back seat. "Leroy say we be fine. He going to meet us there."

"He didn't know about the roadworks." Jack trumps his ace. "Only listens to music, him, not things that matter."

"Could you get out of the car, please, Miss?" the first officer says politely, opening the door for me and failing to completely hide his grin. His mate isn't even trying. "Is this your vehicle?"

"No, Officer. I've just borrowed it."

"Mrs Brown wondered where it had got to, you see. And why half her residents were missing their tea?"

Reggie's furiously polishing his glasses. Jack's pulled his tweed cap so low it looks as if he's wearing it on his face. Ted appears to have dropped something on the floor and Freddie's impersonating a Buddha and keeping shtum. Delroy's the only one who keeps his head.

"Come on, mi man," he tells the policeman. "You can't keep us chatting, you know. We'll be late."

"Might I ask where you're headed?" the officer says.

Reggie slams the glasses back onto his nose and glares.

"None of yours!" he hisses in a hard-boiled way out of the corner of his mouth.

"Are we doing anything wrong, Officer?"

Goldfinger wouldn't have had to mess about with lasers if he'd had Fingers handy. Her stare could have done a lot of damage to 007's man-bits.

"No, Madam," the officer says, "but…"

"Can't pretend we were speeding," Freddie grunts. "Snails were overtaking us. On the inside."

"No, sir, but…"

W e're going to the Stones concert." Fingers changes tack, batting her eyelashes. I can't help but feel she's being a little hopeful here. It might work on Reg, and it never fails to reduce Jack and Ted to grovelling wrecks – but whether it'll have the desired effect on someone young enough to be her grandson is definitely up for debate.

"Rolling Stones?" The officer looks disbelieving.

"Show him, dear," she commands.

The officer whistles as he peruses the precious bits of paper.

"Respect! How did you get them?"

Delroy smiles proudly.

"Still got mi contacts, sonny Jim."

"His grandson works for the promoters," Fingers enlightens the cop. "And he's waiting for us," she adds pointedly.

"But aren't you all a bit too…?" He obviously doesn't want to say the O-word, but *Greystones Residential Home* sign-written across the back of the minibus is a bit of a giveaway.

"Not much older than Rubber Lips and he's on stage," Fingers says crisply.

I pull the officer away from the minibus before he says something he'll regret.

"I did leave Sue a message when I picked up the car keys, but she can't have got it," I tell him softly, so the gang don't hear. "They were so convinced she wouldn't let them go that they had to stage a get-away. And I have to say, she wasn't all that keen on letting them loose on the town. Knows them of old, you see."

"She thought they'd gone off on their own. Worried they'd have an accident, like. None of them have valid driving licences."

Thank goodness for that. We'd never keep track of them if they could disappear on an Away Day whenever they felt inclined.

"It's all right, Officer. I'll look after them. Tell Sue not to worry – I won't let any of them get behind the wheel and I won't let them stay out too late."

I cross my fingers behind my back. Sue isn't the only one who's got their number.

The police car drives away, visibly vibrating with giggles. I get back behind the wheel.

"Good going, kid. Fooled the fuzz. You were taught by the best." Reggie tries to look suitably modest.

"A chip off the old block," says Fingers. "I never let people boss me about. Well done, Jeannie, dear."

"Auntie Muriel, that's the nicest thing you've ever said to me."

And the funny thing is, I'm not being totally ironic. Ⓜ

• •

THE FIRST BOOK I READ…

By the age of six or seven I'd devoured piles of Enid Blyton etc, but the first classic was *Black Beauty*. I was incandescent about the use of that horrible bearing rein."

I LOVE YOU ♥ ANGEL ♥ FLETCHER

The backing singer was the star of the show for me…

By Helen M Walters

The band bounce onto the stage. Tommy Righteous carries his guitar like a jousting shield and faces the audience with every expectation of adulation. But I only have eyes for Angel Fletcher.

Angel is, as my best mate Ian puts it, "only a backing singer" but she's the reason I'm here at our local's live gig night. I always come when Righteous Lights are playing. Not because of Tommy, but because of Angel.

"She'll never look at someone like you, Matt," Ian said earlier on when we were getting ready to come out.

I knew he was right, but I couldn't help dreaming. Angel had captured my

anyway?" Ian said. "You can't exactly go up to her and tell her how you feel, can you? It's way too stalkerish."

Hanging around after the gig and trying to chat her up wasn't really my style. And anyway Ian was probably right. There was no reason someone like her would be interested in me.

But I still wanted to let her know that I appreciated her. Tommy usually took all the glory, and I couldn't help thinking he didn't appreciate Angel's contribution to the band's success as much as he should have done. I wanted Angel to know that she was just as talented.

"The thing is," I said to Ian, "we need to tell people we appreciate them before it's too late. Look at Bowie, look at Tom Petty, and all the other greats we've lost

Her voice rises above Tommy's growl like sunshine above the clouds

heart the very first time the band played The Horse and Groom. It was the way she looked into the crowd when she sang, as though she was actually singing to me personally.

"What are you going to do about it

in the last couple of years. Everyone came out and said how fabulous they were after they were dead. But it was too late then. You need to tell people while they're still around to hear it."

"I don't think Angel's going to die,

mate,' Ian said. "She can't be more than about twenty-five."

"We didn't think George Michael was going to die," I said. "But he did."

So here I am sitting right at the front of the crowd with my pint balanced on my knee listening to the now familiar Righteous Lights set.

They always start off with an upbeat number. Angel smiles and bounces up and down on her toes as she sings. Her voice is pure and clear and offers a pleasing counterpoint to Tommy's gravelly growl.

Then Angel closes her eyes and they move on to a slower, more dreamy number. Tommy keeps his growling to a minimum and her voice rises above his like sunshine above the clouds.

In the next upbeat number, everyone in the pub gets up and dances. I am transported by the beat, by Angel's voice, by the twanging guitars and then, without even realising I'm doing it, I find myself calling out, "I love you, Angel Fletcher!"

Ian turns and grimaces at me, and a couple of others give me curious glances. But my words have been swept away by the cacophony of music. Angel can't possibly have heard what I said above all the noise she's surrounded by on stage.

Eventually my blushes fade and I allow myself to just enjoy the rest of the set. Angel didn't hear what I said, but at least I said it.

But then something amazing happens. During a break between songs Angel grabs her microphone, looks sideways at Tommy and then addresses the crowd.

"I love you too," she says in her lovely clear voice. And she smiles.

Then the music starts again and I can't ask Ian whether he heard it as well or whether I've imagined it. But I spend the rest of the gig on a wave of euphoria.

"Come on, mate," Ian says after the gig, when the obligatory encore and the band's final bows are over.

And it's only then, as we turn to leave the pub, that I realise I'm not Angel's only fan.

I stop dead as I take in the banner being held up by two young lads right at the back of the room.

We love you, Angel Fletcher, it says.

As we leave the pub, all I can do is laugh at myself. And accept Ian's laughter with good grace.

I'm not the only one who loves Angel – and when she said "I love you too" into the crowd, she wasn't talking to me.

But actually that's not important. Angel knows she is loved – and that's all that matters to me. 🅜

THE FIRST BOOK I READ...

The first novel I actually remember reading was *The Weirdstone Of Brisingamen* by Alan Garner, when I was about 10. I loved the amazing sense of adventure as the characters were swept into a fantasy world.

Hidden Treasure

No wonder trade was slow at Margery's charity shop, with the outrageous prices she was charging...

By Christine Sutton

Betty gazed at the rails of limp clothing and pairs of scuffed shoes piled beneath.

"Thanks for stepping in, Betty," Margery said. "There's not much to it. Just be on hand to help where needed – and don't let anyone persuade you to reduce the prices. Being close to Steeple Park means we get some quality items. Like this." She took a brightly coloured jug from a shelf. "Clarice Cliff goes for fortunes on *Bargain Hunt*, so it's a snip at eighty pounds, yet people think because it's a donation we should offer it for peanuts."

"How long's it been here?" Betty asked, eyeing the dusty rim.

"Oh, a few months," Margery answered vaguely. "Why?"

"Well, wouldn't forty in the till be better than eighty gathering dust on a shelf? You've heaps more stuff out back. There's a painting that looks like –"

"This jug is a collector's item," Margery cut in, "we can't just give it away." An elderly man came in, leaning heavily on a stick. "Here's a typical example," she murmured. "He's forever complaining about the prices, yet I saw him loading shopping into a vintage Jaguar last week."

"Well, that hardly makes him rich," Betty reasoned.

"But not poor either," Margery countered. "Anyway, time for tea."

She disappeared into the rear of the shop, leaving Betty with the man.

"Would you like to try anything on?" she asked, as he began sorting through the coats. "There's a cubicle if you'd prefer privacy."

"It's not privacy I need, dear, it's a mortgage." He sighed, selecting a houndstooth jacket. "How does your manager lady think anyone can afford these prices?"

"Goodness!" She gasped, looking at the tag. "You could get a new one for that."

"Exactly. It's quality, yes, but this is a charity shop and I was brought up to believe that charity begins at home."

Betty made a show of peering at the label. "Oh, I really should get my eyes tested. I thought that said seven, but it's really a one, isn't it?"

The man smiled, catching her drift.

"Oh, yes. Ten pounds, that's more like it." He laid his coat on the floor and slipped the jacket on.

"Very dapper," Betty said, smoothing the shoulders.

"Yes, I like it. I'll take it. I'm Joe, by the way," he said, following her to the till.

"Betty," she told him. "I'm standing in for my brother while he's in hospital having his knee fixed. Forty-eight and still playing rugby." She shook her head at the madness of men. Just then Margery ➤

returned with the teas. Joe thrust the money at Betty and quickly hobbled out.

"Don't tell me he actually bought something," Margery said, handing her a mug. "Wonders will never cease. Anyway, that painting you mentioned? I'm checking it out online. You'll be OK here for a while?"

"Of course," Betty said. "I'll be interested to hear what you discover."

Left to her own devices, she went to browse the window display. Her eyes widened at the price on a crystal-beaded gown. Four hundred pounds! What was Margery thinking? These donations might come from people who shopped in swanky malls in town, but the folk who came here weren't so flush.

As she turned away, her toe brushed something on the floor; a mobile phone. It must have fallen from Joe's pocket

"Well, I've got it safe – and to the best of my knowledge your father is, too."

"That's a relief. Thanks. I'll come straight away. Whereabouts are you?"

"It's the charity shop on Calhoon Way," she told him.

"OK, Betty, I'll see you shortly."

Thinking that Joe's son sounded every bit as nice as his dad, she disconnected.

Fifteen minutes later a sporty Jag in racing green pulled up outside. Of course, she thought, as a distinguished looking man in his mid-forties got out, it wasn't his own car Margery had seen Joe loading shopping into, it was his son's.

"Hi," he said, coming inside. "You must be Betty. Roy French."

"Hello, Roy," she said, reaching under the counter for the phone. "There you go."

"Thanks, I'll take it straight round.

"That phone. It's me having the heart attack when folk call to say they've found it"

when he tried on the jacket. She scrolled through the contact list; *Bowls Club, Garden Centre, Dr Keen.* Finding someone called Roy, she pressed call.

"Hello, Dad," said a warm male voice. "How are you?"

"Umm, is that Roy?" Betty asked.

The voice took on a worried note.

"Yes, who's this? Has something happened?"

"No, everything's fine," she assured him. "My name's Betty and I found this phone on the floor of the shop where I'm working. I think it might be Joe's."

There was an exasperated tut.

"That blessed phone. I bought it for him in case of emergencies, but it's me having the heart attack every time someone rings to say they've found it."

Betty chuckled.

Heaven knows how he came to drop it."

"I think it slipped from his pocket when he put his coat on the floor to try on a jacket." She smiled conspiratorially. "We, um, might have misread the price tag, so when the manager came back in he didn't hang around to find out. I mean, look at the price on this." She showed him the label on the brightly coloured jug. Roy inclined his head.

"Actually, that's not far off. I'm an auctioneer at Shelby's and Clarice stuff sells like hotcakes. This could fetch two hundred or more."

Betty gaped at him in surprise. "Really? Goodness. What about the dress there?"

He checked the label on the beaded gown. "Vera Wang's a top designer, so that's not unreasonable. Your manager's on the right track. It's not the prices

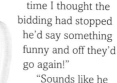

that are wrong, it's the location. If you let me pick out a few pieces, we could see how they fare at auction."

They turned at the sound of Margery's voice. "You were right about this painting, Betty... Oh, sorry, you have a customer."

"Margery, this is Mr French, Joe's son," Betty said. "He works at Shelby's and thinks some of our items might do well at auction."

"No guarantees, of course," Roy cautioned, "but if we set the reserve at what you've already priced them at, you wouldn't lose anything. Perhaps Betty might like to come and see how they fare." He smiled. Betty felt herself colouring.

"Thank you – I'd love to."

"Good. Now, what have we got here?" He took the painting from Margery's hands and placed it on the counter.

"A young man brought it in this morning," Margery explained. "He said his late aunt had left it to us in her will."

"A very nice donation," said Roy.

Betty peered at the artist's name.

"I couldn't be sure, but I thought that said Coetzee," she ventured. "A friend in South Africa has a couple of his early pieces and she said that after he died, the prices went through the roof."

"She's right," Roy agreed. He arched a playful brow. "And that, Betty, means that our auction just got a whole lot more interesting."

Betty sat at her brother's bedside, showing him the photos on her digital camera.

"Imagine, Larry – four thousand pounds," she said excitedly. "This dress alone fetched seven hundred and the jug did well, too. Roy was so clever. Every

time I thought the bidding had stopped he'd say something funny and off they'd go again!"

"Sounds like he knows his stuff," Larry said, wincing as his newly repaired knee made its presence felt. "Margery, too, come to that. What about the painting?"

"That's next week," Betty said. "Roy's set the reserve at five thousand but with interest being shown from South Africa, he reckons it'll fly past that." Her eyes lit up as the man himself came back in carrying a tray of drinks. "I was just telling Larry how brilliant you were today."

"The stuff sold itself really," Roy said modestly. "Still, Margery's pleased."

"I bet," Larry laughed. "Four grand for stuff that sat in the shop for months?"

"Did you tell him our plan?" Roy asked, handing Betty a coffee.

She shook her head. "The idea is that once you're back at work, Larry, I'll come in a couple of times a week and take photos of any donations with potential, then take them to Roy for assessment."

His lips twitched. "He can't just come in and see them for himself?"

"Oh, no," Roy smiled, his gaze resting on Betty, "far too busy."

Betty felt a little glow inside. Margery wasn't the only one pleased with today's result. She was more than happy with her "lot", too! ⓂⓌ

. . . .

THE FIRST BOOK I READ...

I must have been 10 when I first "met" Jane Eyre. Charlotte Bronte's strong characters woven into a storyline that seemed impossible to end happily, yet somehow did, made thrilling reading.

And There Was Hope

With their home bombed and a baby on the way, how will Lily and Frank cope in wartime London?

By Elaine F Chong

Frank picked his way across the broken ground, the remains of his home lying in pieces around him. The bombing raid on the city last night had left too many lives in tatters.

The newspapers were calling it "The Blitz" and this morning's editions showed a photograph of the London skyline with buildings ablaze.

At least Lily was safe, he thought.

They'd stumbled out of the Underground shelter when it was daylight to a scene of such devastation that it was hard to fathom where their home had once been.

Lily had cried out in fear and desperation.

"Oh, Frank! It's all gone."

He'd gathered her into his arms, →

stroked her hair, tried to reassure her.

"We've still got each other," he'd told her. "It's just bricks and mortar."

"It was our home!" she'd wailed loudly. "Where will we go now?"

A kind neighbour had helped him guide her to a street where the houses were still standing. She offered them hot, sweet tea and a place to rest until Frank could find them somewhere to stay.

Lily had sunk gratefully onto a chair in the cramped kitchen, and Frank

One of the men had brought a wheelbarrow and a couple of shovels.

"Which floor were you living on?" he asked Frank. "Some of your furniture might still be intact, but there's not much hope if you lived upstairs."

Frank breathed a sigh of relief. He and Lily had occupied two rooms at the back of the house on the ground floor. They'd been a real find. The rooms were clean and in a good state of repair. He and Lily had considered themselves lucky at the

"We need to take it steady. Don't want the rest of the house falling on our heads"

had promised her that he'd "sort it".

It wasn't really safe to go back and search through the rubble, but he knew that if he could find any of their belongings still in one piece, it would go a long way to making Lily feel more secure.

An ARP warden suddenly appeared.

"You can't just go climbing over there," he told Frank.

"It's my home," Frank said. "I've got to see if I can find any of our stuff."

The man clapped him on the shoulder in a sympathetic way.

"It might have been your home yesterday, son," he said. "Hang on and I'll get some of the boys to give you a hand. You need to go careful."

He whistled and a group of men in Home Guard uniforms made their way over from where they were searching through the debris of another house that had been hit.

"Find anything?" he asked them.

Cheerlessly they shook their heads.

The ARP warden turned back to Frank.

"Family lost their dog; they think it ran back into the house." He gave a wan smile. "Any luck, it'll fetch up here and be right as rain."

time because a lot of the houses in the narrow London streets near the river were rat-infested and damp.

"We haven't got much," he told the man, "but if I can find anything that's still usable then I'll be happy."

The front of the house had taken the worst of the blast, but it looked like the back walls were still standing. Amongst the broken brickwork, Frank could see the supporting beams still holding up what was left of the first floor.

The ARP warden told them to wait in the road while he tried to find a way through. "We'll need to take it slow and steady," he warned. "We don't want the rest of the house falling on our heads."

When he was satisfied that they could remove the debris safely, he motioned to them to join him and they started to clear a path. The men formed a line. It was painfully slow. The wheelbarrow was filled to overflowing again and again.

As the morning wore on, other people joined them in the street, everyone painstakingly sorting through the wreckage of their homes – the wreckage of their lives. Frank was moved by their courage and their tenacity. He thought

sadly of Lily, now heavy with child, mourning the loss of her home, scared and probably feeling lost and alone without him.

Suddenly, there was a shout from the man at head of the line. "I've found a door!"

"He's found a door!" the other men echoed.

Frank pushed past them. "It's the bedroom," he told them. He turned the handle, but the door didn't budge; he moved to put his shoulder against it, but the ARP warden pulled him back.

"Just hold on," he said. "You put your weight against that door and shove and anything could happen. It's the doorframe, you see. It's helping to hold up the bricks, and the bricks are holding up the floor joists. You barge through and you could bring the whole place down."

warden leaned forward and peered through the gap.

"Well, the bed's had it, but the chest of drawers looks OK. I reckon you could salvage the bedding and few more bits and pieces."

"Can we get the door open?" Frank asked him.

"We can try."

It took two of them to force a way past the broken pieces of ceiling piled up behind the door, and when Frank saw the state of the bedroom, he felt despairing. The was a gaping hole in the ceiling and the contents of the room on the first floor were scattered everywhere, everything smashed to pieces, and covered in plaster and brick dust.

"If we're going to salvage anything, we'll have to get a move on," the ARP warden told him. "I don't like the look of

The walls began to shake. Thirty seconds later there came a rumbling sound

"So, what do we do?" Frank demanded, frustration making him impatient.

The man with the wheelbarrow joined them. "We could try knocking out a few bricks in the wall here." He indicated some loose bricks near the top of the door. "If we remove a few of them, we can see if it's safe."

The ARP warden agreed. He took hold of one of the shovels and used it as a hammer. After just a handful of sharp blows, the bricks fell into the room. The

that back wall. Ten minutes, and that's it."

Frank and the other men set to work at once. They stripped the bed, piled everything that wasn't broken into the centre of the bed sheets and carried them into the road. Then Frank and the ARP warden hurriedly half-carried and half-dragged the chest of drawers through the bedroom door as the walls began to shake. Thirty seconds later, there was a rumbling sound, and the house collapsed.

Frank stood in the street covered ➤

from head to foot in dirt and dust, with all his worldly goods piled up next to him. Tears stung his eyes, and he wiped them away with the back of his hand.

The ARP warden slung a comforting arm about his shoulder.

The woman who had taken Lily in was hanging out washing in the small back yard. She smiled when she saw Frank.

"Your missus is sleeping. She's a good girl. Told me you work for the railways."

Frank nodded. "I wanted to join

The sight of her, small and vulnerable, filled him with a fierce determination

"You've done well, son," he told him. "Other folks would have just walked away."

"Well? I've got a wife, and a baby on the way, and this is everything we own," Frank said, indicating the chest of drawers and the bundle of bed sheets.

"It doesn't look much," the warden agreed, "but at least you're alive."

Well, there was no arguing with that, Frank thought to himself. He asked to borrow the wheelbarrow, promising to return it the following day. With help, he loaded their only surviving piece of furniture onto it and stuffed the sheets and everything wrapped inside them into the drawers. It took all his strength to push the wheelbarrow back to the house where he'd left Lily earlier that day.

up, like my pals did, but they told me I couldn't. Said I was in an essential service."

"It is," she said. She laid a friendly hand on his arm. "We all have to do our bit and that means keeping the trains running as well." She quickly went on, "I've told your Lily you can both stay here till you get something sorted. My boy's with the First Infantry Division so his room's empty for now."

Frank hesitated. "I don't know how to thank you, Mrs…?"

She laughed. "Call me Ethel." She gave him a little push. "You'd better go and see if she's woken up. She's been worried sick you wouldn't come back."

After removing his boots and brushing

off the worst of the dust and dirt, he tiptoed up the stairs. Lily lay on her side in a narrow, single bed in a small room at the back of the house. Her mouth was open and she was gently snoring. The sight of her, small and vulnerable, filled him with a fierce determination. He had to find somewhere for them to live, somewhere safe.

Early the following day, after spending a night sleeping on the floor wrapped up in a blanket, Frank got ready to go to work. Lily insisted that she was fine and would spend the day with Ethel washing the sheets and sorting through the belongings Frank had managed to salvage from the wreckage.

"Everything'll clean up just fine, Frank," she told him.

"Are you sure you're OK?" he asked, peering at her anxiously.

She put her hand to the small of her back and grimaced. "I think I might have been better off sleeping on the floor. That mattress had more hard lumps in it than a bag of spanners."

Frank forced a smile.

"I'll find us a place we can call our own, Lily. I promise."

Even though some of the Underground stations had been turned into makeshift air raid shelters, the trains were still running, and Frank hardly had time to think about the precarious future that he and Lily were now facing.

At the end of day, he slowly made his way back to Ethel's house, hoping against hope that they would find a way to stay together, because if he didn't find rooms for them soon, he would have to ask Lily to return home to her mum and dad.

She would be safer away from the dangers of living in London, scurrying for shelter through the darkened streets, and never knowing what horrors daylight

hours would bring – but he was certain that she would simply refuse to go.

Ethel met him at the door. She looked flushed and excited.

"Hard day, Frank?" she asked him.

"I've had better," he said, puzzled at the pleased expression on her face.

"Lily's got a surprise for you."

"A surprise?" he repeated.

Suddenly, from somewhere inside the house, a thin wail could be heard.

At first, Frank felt only confusion, but as the noise continued to flow from the open window, he understood what Ethel had been trying to tell him. He kicked off his boots and ran into the house with Ethel close on his heels.

She grabbed at his sleeve to slow him. "Baby came a few weeks too soon, but you mustn't worry."

Lily was sitting up bed. She looked utterly exhausted. In her arms, nestled in a blanket, was a tiny baby.

"We've got a daughter, Frank," she said and offered him the precious bundle.

Frank just stood there. Ethel quietly moved between them, took the baby from Lily and gently handed her Frank.

"She's a beauty," she told him. "Lily's done the hard bit. Now you have to give her a name."

Frank gazed down at the tiny baby cradled against his chest.

"I thought we'd lost everything," he said, his voice breaking. "But I was wrong." He looked up and tears shone in his eyes. "We're calling her Hope. It's all I have to give her – but I think it's going to be enough." 🅜🅦

THE FIRST BOOK I READ...

I think I was about six or seven when I read *The Secret Garden* by Frances Hodgson Burnett. It ignited a lifelong interest in stories of secrets and mysteries.

The Centre Of The Universe

The little creature had come from far across the galaxy, but would they be able to take her into their hearts?

By Jo Styles

The little alien lay under a table in our lounge.

It dipped its three-pronged hand into a plate of chocolate cake and slapped it on the wall. It made smears left and right as I watched.

Icing had already stained its purple romper suit.

"Should we let it make a mess like this?" My husband, bending down low, peered at the creature. "Why did we pick this one from the catalogue anyway? In real life it looks like a rabbit crossed with a potato. I'm sure they enhance those videos and photos, you know."

"I thought it looked cute." I crossed my arms. "I think it still does." David couldn't hide his frown as laughter bubbled up into my throat. "Look, it's drawing a little

The machine gave me a start, blurting out alien verbs and nouns, if aliens even use those. It actually sounded a lot like a chicken in a flap – Cluck cluck cluck.

"Is it drawing our house now?" I couldn't help but smile.

Our doctor had advised us to adopt something since neither of us could have children naturally. Birth rates had fallen dramatically on earth for various reasons. We might have chosen a dog or a cat but since the discovery of Planet 668P11 other avenues could now be explored by anybody who didn't mind filling in online forms and paying a massive fee. This felt like a bit of an adventure – to me at least – and since Planet 668P11's sun would die very soon the population of its orphanages needed re-homing along with the rest of its citizens.

"We should never have given it that

Our doctor advised us to adopt and the alien children needed somewhere to go

picture of a tree. Do they have those where it comes from?"

He leaned down a little further to study the smears cutting across our stripy wallpaper. He switched on the translator he held and started to type.

"What are you asking it?"

"I'm asking it to stop, of course."

cake," sighed David.

"The instruction manual said it likes sweet things," I replied, "and I thought it would be a nice way to say Hello and welcome to our family.

He gave a loud huff. "It's not even drawing our house. Look, it's missed off the porch entirely." ➙

"The truth is we were fooled by a TV ad, so I'm going to get them to take it back"

"Well, the agency did say it lived with another couple before us."

"I think I can see why they returned it. I'm afraid I'm just not warming to it, darling. Maybe this was a mistake?"

My pulse thundered in my ears. If we couldn't have a human child I had no objections to raising one from another world. "If we'd had a baby of our own we wouldn't just send it back, would we?" I pointed out. "We'd have to persevere no matter how much cake it flung about. It's probably just a phase anyway. They go through those, don't they?"

David turned towards the door regardless. "I think I'll just call the agency anyway. Maybe this is just a bad one. You know, a bit of a lemon. It did try to eat the rug, and it completely destroyed its new bed before it even slept in it. Maybe they have a nicer one in stock. I mean, think how often we go away and have to switch rooms at hotels because we have a terrible view? And think of that furniture we returned because it wasn't the colour it looked on screen. Yes, I think I'll go and give them a ring."

The creature snorted when David had gone. Its lips rolled back in a snarl.

"Sorry about that." I dropped to my knees and crawled towards it across the carpet. "He always thinks there's a better one – a better settee, a nicer TV. I was never really sure he was right for children really… or an extraterrestrial."

The creature sniffed and scratched one butter-icing soiled finger across its furry neck. Its huge pointed ears twitched.

"It might have helped if you'd used the cake fork." I pointed to the utensil cast aside then I offered a tissue so the creature could wipe its hands. "If you behave really well at lunch maybe he'll change his mind about you. Use your napkin, keep your mitts clean and don't eat any more carpet," I suggested.

I really needed the translator, only the little thing looked at me with such conviction I felt sure I'd wriggled my way through the language barrier.

Splat went the sandwich. It fell to pieces when it dropped down the wall of the kitchen. Flakes of salmon flew everywhere. In its high chair the creature smiled with teeth as pointed as a shark's. I'd thought a few sandwiches might be safer than liquids. Still, lunch wasn't going too well.

"It's young," I said hurriedly. "It hasn't learned how to eat properly yet."

"That's not all it hasn't learned. I found teeth marks in the skirting board." David let his own sandwich drop to his plate with a slap. "Yes, I'm glad I did it now."

"Did what?"

"I told the agency to come and pick it up. They'll be here at four. I asked for an earlier appointment but apparently they're busy. I expect they have more rejects to redistribute." He gave me a worried look. "I'm sorry but this creature's nothing like how I imagined and I read the entire manual online three times. Please, don't make me feel worse and remind me that things might be different if it was a baby. It's simply not. It's not our flesh and blood. It's not in any way a part of who we are. The truth is we were fooled by a TV ad and some computer generated trickery." His chair scraped back. "I think I'll call the agency again and demand they come and collect it straight away."

I watched him stride off, a word on my lips. That word was "No!" and I said it so loudly my ears rang.

He whirled about. "Sorry? Pardon?"

"Well, don't I have any say in this? Maybe you ought to go instead, David. Yes, maybe you're the reject here. Maybe you're the one who doesn't fit in."

He blinked. "Are you serious?" ➤

"Yes I am."

"You want me to leave over…" He stabbed a finger towards the creature's seat – only then he gave a start. "Where's it gone?"

While we'd been distracted it had disappeared. Its manual said our little visitor could climb anything and could move at speed.

"We've upset her arguing in front of her. She knows you want to get rid of her, that she's going to lose her home again."

"What do you mean, she? The manual didn't say anything about it being a boy or a girl."

"We need to find her, David." I hunted about in the kitchen cupboards in case

"I don't believe it, she's eating butterflies now!" David exclaimed in disgust when her snacking habits changed. "Some of those are an endangered species. She's a vandal. She has no feelings…and why am I still calling it… a her?"

Maybe butterflies tasted better than salmon sandwiches? She ran leaping and lunging and snapping her jaws like something demented. Out of mid air she snatched a Tortoiseshell, a red Admiral then three Cabbage Whites. She moved on to a Common Blue…

Chomp. Chomp. Chomp.

"Please, stop doing that. Leave

The lonely little alien had already lost a planet and two sets of parents

she'd decided on a game akin to hide and seek while David hurried out into the hall.

"I can see her," came his call from the lounge. "She's outside."

Once in the lounge, I raced out through the patio doors into the sunshine of the garden. "I'm so sorry," I called.

The creature crawled to the middle of the grass, her gangly limbs drawing in. When I reached her I ached to stroke her furry head to make her feel better. I did try to touch her flat moon-like face but she shot away at tremendous speed.

"Wait!" I cried in alarm.

Across the garden she gambolled ahead of me. Sometimes on all fours, sometimes upright she nosed into the flowerbeds, tearing off geranium heads with her teeth. She tossed the lot aside.

them alone!" I chased in her wake. "Just because you've been hurt doesn't mean you have to hurt somebody else."

She whirled about, her thin arms wide. She blinked up at me, sniffled then swiped at her big amber eyes.

Like little jewels of sorrow her tears had a luminous silver hue. She mewled in her throat like a cat as she grieved, her cheeks still bulging around her multi-coloured meal.

I crouched down to her level then needed to swallow before I could speak. "We shouldn't have said all those hurtful things in front of you. That was mean and horrible. I know you've already lost a planet and two sets of parents.

"Maybe you want to reject us now. I wouldn't blame you. But I would like you to stay with me, if you'd like that at all?"

Asking her what she wanted suddenly seemed like a good idea to me. In reply, she opened her mouth and wings fluttered.

All the butterflies I thought she'd swallowed down took flight. A cascade of bright colours streamed into the blue of the sky. As they escaped she crawled across the emerald grass right into my arms.

She snuggled close to my ear and whispered a word that left me reeling. I gazed into her glowing eyes. I could never have given birth to a daughter so hairy or to one with such expressive ears but love poured through me.

"Do you like the name Chloe?" I asked.

I don't know if she understood but she hung on so tightly as David loomed above us. That's when a familiar voice called, "Hello, Mr and Mrs Stevens, it's me, Nancy from the agency."

She must have come down the drive then heard the ruckus in the garden. David hurried over to the side gate and let her in. Three men in black followed at her back. They were all from Alien Adoption Services.

"They can't take her, I won't let them," I said to David as they surrounded me and little Chloe like lions about to pounce.

"They have to," he said. "They've already sent a refund and they've cancelled all the paperwork." He glanced back at the three burly men behind him. They wore resigned expressions and one carried a shiny metal cage.

Nancy from the agency scurried closer. "Oh don't worry, this happens all the time. These creatures can be challenging at any age. It is very difficult to integrate another species."

I raised my head and set my shoulders back. "You're not listening to me. She isn't going anywhere. Say it," I urged Chloe.

"Say what you said to me earlier."

Glaring at David, she pulled her long pointed ears down until they lay low and flat. "M-u-m-m-y. M-u-m-m-y," she croaked out like a tiny frog.

David's jaw unhinged as Nancy gasped. "Well, I never! She's never done that before."

Chloe made another sound then, a low, deep grumbling rumble that shook her shoulders and made her round belly jiggle. "D-a-d-d-y?" she said.

She posed it like a question as if she knew it was in doubt.

David looked like he wanted to pinch himself to check he wasn't dreaming.

We had always imagined one day some little mite would call us Mummy and Daddy.

Only we'd thought it would never happen. It was well beyond our reach.

David's breathing grew shallow and he sank down to his knees.

"Daddy?" he repeated in a whisper as above him Nancy from the agency gave a knowing smile.

They do say sometimes it's hard to bond with your newborn but you never give up trying, do you? You have to believe one day they will become the centre of your universe.

"Daddy," David said one more time. Only now it didn't sound like a question he was asking. It sounded like an answer he'd just found. 🅜

THE FIRST BOOK I READ...

I can't remember the first novel I read but it was likely one by the Pullein-Thompson sisters, Josephine, Diana and Christine. They wrote books about the kind of horsey adventures I wanted to go on but my parents couldn't afford.

Kind Hearts And Coronets

The Coronation was a time for everyone to come together but Jenny felt compelled to keep her distance

By Barbara Dynes

Jenny watched her workmates in the staff room mirror. The break between films was coming up soon, so they were dolling themselves up. As usherettes, all three of them were required to sell ices. This was the highlight of the day for Shirley and Joan – their bright lipstick and mascara a vital part. But not for Jenny.

"You should make an effort, Jen," said Shirley. "Pete seems to have a soft spot for you. Don't you like him?"

Jenny shrugged. "Like" was putting it mildly. A young Gregory Peck, the others called Pete, the Regal's trainee projectionist. She, too, thought he was really dishy, but wouldn't admit to it.

Like her, he was new to his job and when Jenny was on ices she'd get the shivers as he trained the spotlight on her,

Shirley frowned, turning to Jenny.

"Got your Union Jack ready for next week's Coronation, Jen?"

Jenny laughed, grateful to Shirley for changing the subject. Joan could be quite blunt sometimes.

Later, after filling their ice cream trays, they stood apart in front of the screen facing the audience. On came the spotlight. Dazzled at first, Jenny blinked, then blushed, her heart hammering. The clamouring began.

"Strawberry, please, Miss!"

Jenny grinned at her first customer. Anything to take her mind off the man operating that spotlight. She needed to stay detached – cool, like these ices. No way could she risk having feelings for another man ever again.

Anyway, Joan was probably right. Why on earth should Pete be interested in her?

The gorgeous "Mr Peck" was interested in her! Then she came down to earth

sometimes for a little too long. Then the light would catch Shirley's immaculate blonde curls or Joan's thick make-up, making Jenny feel scruffy and a bit sad. But, secretly, she was finished with men.

"A soft spot for Jenny?" Joan repeated, throwing her lipstick on the table. "I really don't think so!"

But later, as she walked to the bus in the dark, looking forward to her day off tomorrow, she heard her name called. Instinctively, she knew it was Pete. Her first thought was to run, but he was too close. She stopped under a streetlight.

"Coming round to Muriel's next week to see the Coronation?" he asked. "We're

all squeezing into her front room."

His brown eyes seemed enormous and his smile warm in the eerie orange light. The gorgeous "Mr Peck" was interested in her! Then she came back down to earth.

"I'm sorry, Pete, I can't. I'm going with Mum to her friend's house," she said quickly. "It's all arranged."

She knew her mother wouldn't mind a bit if she went elsewhere. But it was better to steer clear of Pete.

"Oh, pity! Just thought I'd ask," he said cheerily.

Jenny felt bad; there was a resignation in his expression as he turned away. Maybe other girls had turned him down? ➙

On the bus, Jenny thought about the Coronation. She would have liked to watch it on Muriel's television; these big occasions were more fun with a crowd.

Yet she'd loved going to the Festival of Britain a couple of years ago, and that had been just the two of them. She and Ben had gone on a day trip soon after they got engaged.

The train was packed, but she'd flaunted her emerald ring for all she was worth, her head in the clouds most of the day, dreaming of her future wedding. Two bridesmaids in pale pink, pink and white roses and a fairy-tale meringue of a dress. She smiled now. Both being in low-paid jobs, heaven knew how they'd have paid for any of it! But such a lovely dream…

She studied her left hand, now bare of rings of any kind, recalling Ben's arm around her that day as they gazed up at

Mr Parsons was a stickler for the girls taking their overalls home to wash on their day off. And yesterday a tot had splodged chocolate ice cream down hers.

She blamed Pete. Had he not put her in such a dither earlier, she might have remembered and gone back for it. Too bad – she'd just have to put up with a moaning Mr P.

Jenny leaned over her daughter's cot. She'd been longing to do this all day. Blonde, blue-eyed and beautiful and just ten months old, Alice was sound asleep.

Jenny touched the tiny hand. Sometimes she could hardly believe this baby was hers. Ben, fleeing with all his tame excuses when he knew she was pregnant, hadn't a clue what he was missing. To think, he'd never even seen his child! Someone said he was now hiking around France. Well, good luck to him!

Now everyone would know. She felt almost relieved. He'd get the message

the Skylon, a slim cigar-shaped beacon stretching up to the sky. She had felt so good and Ben seemed so happy.

She sighed. A few months later he was gone, out of her life. *I need to travel, see the world…* Well, that was his excuse.

"Not all men are like Ben," her mum tried to tell her. But who would be interested in her now? Certainly not the gorgeous Pete – not once he knew about Alice.

Arriving home, she called to her mother. "Everything OK, Mum?"

"Fine. Got your overall?"

"Oh, I forgot!"

Jenny groaned as she dashed upstairs.

Next morning, her mother having gone out, Jenny was getting Alice ready for a walk in the park when the doorbell rang. The milkman, come for his money. Clutching Alice in just vest and nappy, she grabbed her purse and hurried downstairs.

But it was not Jim, their cheery milkman. A stunned Jenny gazed at the grinning girl in a bright yellow dress. Joan!

She watched the grin fade as Joan stared at Alice and began to stutter.

"Er – you forgot your overall." She thrust a bag at Jenny. "Shirley got your address from the office and – and – as you live quite near me…"

Jenny muttered her thanks as Alice, squirming in her arms, began to cry. Now her secret was well and truly out.

"Won't you come in?" she said stiffly.

"No thanks – can't stop. Lovely baby! Whose is it?" Joan beamed, trying to sound casual but not succeeding.

Jenny took a deep breath.

"She's mine. This is Alice." There was no way she was going to lie about her precious daughter. "Her dad and I were engaged, but…" Her voice trailed off. Why should she explain herself to Joan?

"Don't say it!" Joan chimed in. "Men, eh? Must go – see you soon!"

Joan grabbed her bike from by the gate and waved merrily as she rode off, no doubt to spread the gossip at work.

Jenny kissed her fretful baby. Now everyone would know, including Pete. She felt almost relieved. At least he'd get the message and move on.

Back at work the next day, no one mentioned or even hinted about Alice. Joan seemed much more sociable; no doubt realising that Pete, knowing about the baby, would now look elsewhere.

But Jenny felt no shame, just pride. No child was more cherished than Alice; people could think what they liked.

When Muriel, Mr Parsons' secretary, came round to ask how many were coming to her house to see the Coronation, Jenny took a gamble.

"Can you squeeze another one in?"

"Sure. Look forward to seeing you all! Oh – Mum says could you bring a few sandwiches, please?"

After she left, Jenny waited nervously. Joan – or even Shirley – would surely mention Alice now? But no, they resumed their earlier argument about Debbie Reynolds' age. Jenny sent up a little prayer of gratitude to the star of the Regal's current film, *Singin' In The Rain,* for looking about sixteen.

The day of the Coronation was damp and dull. Jenny waved goodbye to Alice and her mum, who couldn't wait to show her granddaughter off to her pal. Then she walked to Muriel's little terraced house.

The front room was already crammed with people – settee, chairs and hardly a square of linoleum floor to be seen. Taking her place in front of the tiny screen, she spotted Pete clutching a beer and being plied with sandwiches by Joan.

"No, thanks, I can't stand fish paste!" he said loudly, glancing around. Jenny smiled at him. But he ignored her, turning back to Joan. Snubbed, Jenny suddenly wished she was anywhere but here.

Biting her lip, she stared blankly at the television, where Richard Dimbleby was spouting about little Prince Charles, with his grandmother in Westminster Abbey. Phew – the atmosphere might be tense there, but for Jenny it was nearly as bad in this stuffy room.

Pete knew about Alice, then. Joan had obviously told him that she, Jenny, came with the label "unmarried mother". Well, he could still be friendly, couldn't he? People around her were getting excited.

"Cor, love that woman's hat!" someone shrieked, as the Coronation progressed. ➜

"Her coach is made of real gold, you know –"

Suddenly a loud sizzling sound came from the television, followed by a bang. The little screen went black. Groans filled the room as Muriel's mother charged through the sprawling bodies towards the set and attempted to shake it vigorously. To no avail.

"This has happened before, I'm afraid," she announced breathlessly.

"Uncle Fred's, ten, Parsley Road – two roads away! He won't mind!" yelled Muriel, taking charge. "Come on!"

Jenny found herself out in the rain with the others, in two minds about going to Uncle Fred's. She felt strangely depressed.

"Coming, Jenny?" It was Pete. "Shirley

Pete raised his eyebrows. He didn't know about Alice.

"You have a baby?"

"Yes. Her father and I were engaged, but then he broke it off."

"How are you coping?"

"OK, actually – Mum has her while I'm at the pictures, as she calls it. Alice is beautiful," she added defiantly.

"I'm sure she is!" He laughed. "It seems we were at cross purposes –"

"True!" Jenny replied, as they turned into Fred's driveway. "Our workmates are not the gossipmongers we took them for."

She frowned, feeling guilty about Joan. It had been wrong to judge her so harshly.

Later, in Fred's spacious living room, Jenny felt quite choked as the crown was placed on the young queen's head. Everyone cheered, a giggling Joan did a

"Our workmates are clearly not the gossip mongers we took them for..."

is bringing Joan. Sorry I couldn't talk in there but Joan has drunk far too much –"

"Poor Joan!" Jenny's mood lifted.

"Pity I haven't got my new motorbike yet. I'm giving cars a miss since…" Pete trailed off as they began to walk. "I do understand you not wanting to go out with me, Jenny."

Jenny frowned. "What d'you mean?"

"Oh! Has Dave, the other projectionist, not let on about me?" Jenny shook her head. "I was a fool. I stupidly got in with a gang back in my home town and we stole a couple of cars. It was all in the papers. I moved here to start again. Mr Parsons was willing to give me a chance."

Jenny took a deep breath.

"But I had no idea! No, I steered clear of you because of my baby," she added.

knees-up in the middle of the room and Fred's spaniel barked approval.

Pete, sitting next to Jenny, smiled.

"Weighs a ton, that crown, I reckon. Her Maj will need to take one step at a time." He squeezed Jenny's hand. "That applies to us, too, eh? Life is not guaranteed to run that smoothly for any of us, even for a Queen."

Jenny grinned. Pete was willing to give her a chance; she felt the same. **MW**

• •

THE FIRST BOOK I READ…

Aged around 10, one of the first novels I read was *Little Women* by Louisa M. Alcott. I was fascinated by Alcott's brilliant characterisation of the four sisters – especially Jo.

Chocolate Reindeer

Ingredients (Makes 4)

- ◆ **115g milk chocolate chips**
- ◆ **40g unsalted butter**
- ◆ **25g golden syrup**
- ◆ **50g toasted rice cereal**
- ◆ **4 large chocolate buttons, halved**
- ◆ **4 salted pretzels**
- ◆ **White piping icing**
- ◆ **4 red candy-coated sweets**

1 Put all but 8 chocolate chips in a saucepan with the butter and syrup and heat very gently until melted. Remove from the heat, stir well and mix in the cereal until well coated.

2 Line a board with baking parchment. Divide the mixture into 4 equal piles on the parchment. Use 2 dessertspoons to form each into a head shape. Carefully push in the chocolate button halves to resemble ears and chill for about an hour until set.

3 Carefully peel the reindeer from the paper and place on a serving board or plate. Gently snap the pretzels in half and lay on top of the chocolate ears. Pipe the eyes with white icing and top with reserved chocolate chips. Pipe a dot to stick on the noses and antlers, and finish each with a piped smile. Serve as soon after decorating as possible.

RECIPE AND FOOD STYLING: KATHRYN HAWKINS PHOTOGRAPHY: LIGHTHOUSE PHOTOGRAPHY

HAPPY (M)ENDING!

A whole lifetime's worth of memories cluttered the attic, but would they take them with them when they moved?

By Claire Buckle

As soon as I let myself in through the front door I heard Mum and Dad's voices from the lounge.

"There won't be enough room. You'll have to donate some to the charity shop," Mum said.

"Why should I get rid of my fishing books when you've cookery books dating back to the dark ages?" Dad retorted.

It crossed my mind that he might've be teasing Mum, hoping she would rise to the bait, if you'll excuse the pun.

I took a deep breath and, with a cheery "hello," walked into the room. My parents were standing in front of half empty bookshelves and surrounded by partly filled cardboard boxes.

"Ah, Sharon," Mum said. "Tell your father there won't be space in the bungalow to house his obsolete library."

Dad puffed up his chest. "I am not disposing of perfectly good books."

"When did you last go fishing?" Mum said, head on one side and hands on her not insubstantial hips.

Dad picked up a tatty cookery book and waved it in the air. From his expression, it was as though he had found a piece of missing evidence. "And when did you last bake a cake?"

"Let's try and solve this calmly," I said. Perhaps Dad wasn't teasing after all.

As a child I wasn't aware they argued. There were never any big rows, even though they weren't what you'd call a lovey-dovey couple. If you're of an age to

remember, think Grandma and Grandpa from *The Waltons* TV series, but from Wolverhampton rather than Virginia. In other words, the affection was there, just bubbling under the surface.

However, recently I'd noticed friction between them and I wondered if their decision to move was a good idea. But the upkeep of the house was becoming a worry. Tim and I helped out when we could, but we worked full-time and had our teenage daughters, Holly and Abby, to care for. So, it seemed an ideal solution when my parents told us they were moving to a newly built bungalow with a manageable garden.

I forced a smile. "How much more is there to pack?"

"Well, he's not even started on the shed," Mum said, accusingly.

Dad merely raised his eyebrows and uttered, "Sewing room." The unsaid words, *I rest my case*, hung in the air.

"All right. I admit I've fair bit to do in there," Mum said.

I was getting impatient. I hadn't taken a half day's holiday to come and listen to them squabbling. "Look, how about I check out the loft?"

Dad knees were dodgy and Mum's rheumatism had been playing up lately, so I didn't want either of them clambering up the ladder.

"Goodness knows what's been shoved up there over the years," Mum grumbled, as we left Dad leafing through a hardback on deep-sea fishing.

I sympathised with Mum in some respects. Although he used to enjoy a lengthy jaunt to the nearest lake for a few hours contemplation over a fishing rod, I couldn't recall him ever stepping onto a boat, let alone emulating Ernest Hemmingway. Then again, →

Mum was more at home with a microwave than the oven these days.

I pulled down the loft ladder and climbed up. Under the harsh strip light I surveyed the scene.

Umpteen boxes were piled on top of each other and vied for space alongside objects shrouded in dusty blankets and threadbare sheets. I exhaled through puffed cheeks. Tim and I would need at least a weekend to get this lot cleared!

I decided it would be best to have a quick rummage inside several boxes and try to prioritise what I thought Mum and Dad would want to keep. The first one I looked in contained musty smelling clothes. From the style they probably dated back more than fifteen years.

No sooner had I decided they were would want them but Holly and Abby might like them put by for them.

By the time I'd sorted through many more boxes, I'd had enough for one day. The rest, along with the small pieces of furniture, would have to wait.

I swiped a grubby hand across my sweaty forehead pleased with what I'd achieved. As I glanced round, four small claw-like wooden feet peeping out beneath a faded candy-striped flannelette sheet caught my eye.

I remembered how, as a small child, Mum would tuck me up in bed each night beneath heavy blankets and a cosy sheet that smelled of fresh air rather than scented conditioner. I laid my hand on the soft material. If it hadn't been dusty,

Under the old sheet was a walnut sewing box, scratched and with rusty hinges

destined for the skip, when I had a flashback to my childhood and the "rag bag" Mum used to keep on a hook in the shed. She'd fill the sack with unwanted clothes or off-cuts of material from her sewing, ready for the rag and bone man. Perhaps, like so many people these days, I was guilty of chucking things away when they could be recycled. Maybe, if I ran them through the wash, the clothes could go to charity rather than landfill.

There was part of a tea set in another box. Decorated with red roses and gold scalloped edges, I recalled seeing the same cups and saucers in several TV dramas over the years, but never on my parents' table. Mum must have picked them up at a boot sale, despite her penchant for serving builders' brew in sturdy mugs. Still, the bone china pieces were dainty and had that fashionable vintage look. I doubted Mum and Dad

I'd have put it against my cheek. It was then that I realised how hard it must be for Mum and Dad to let go of possessions. The books might be of no practical use any more but they were bound to a more active past. No wonder the move was causing a bit of tension.

I lifted the sheet. Underneath, was a walnut sewing box, the lid scratched and with water damage, but with a distinctive carved swirling design around the edges. I knelt down and ran my fingers along the rough groves. It certainly wasn't a professional job, but on closer inspection I realised the swirls were actually the entwined initials, SAR. I frowned. If it were Mum's box then surely the letters would have been SDC, Susan Daphne Collins.

Baffled, I opened the lid, which I only just managed to catch as it came away from its rusty hinges. I put it on the floor and lifted out the tray containing several cotton reels, a dented steel thimble and a pair of pinking sheers. In the space below were some folded up pieces of material and an old Simplicity dress pattern.

I had to smile. My girls would love the orange paisley print on the bell-sleeved maxi dress. At once I remembered seeing a photo in one of the albums of Mum wearing it to a dinner and dance.

At the bottom of the box was a newspaper. The Tanbury Times, dated 25th August 1960, the week of my parents' wedding and the town in which they lived when first married. I turned the pages, glancing at the news items… *Council house hopes for local families*, and *Thug coshes shopkeeper*. Maybe the world hadn't changed that much, I mused.

It was when I came to the middle pages that I stopped and stared. There was a photograph of Mum and Dad on their wedding day!

Wedding of the Week ran the headline. A paragraph below read, *Congratulations to newlyweds Bobby and Susie Collins. The pretty, green-eyed bride looked lovely and as radiant as the sunny day in a dress of white satin and taffeta, which she made herself. A headdress of pearls framed her heart-shaped face. The groom, handsome in a dark grey suit, sported a pink rose in his buttonhole to match those in the bridal bouquet. All of us at The Tanbury Times predict a Happy Ever After for the couple.*

I couldn't wait to show Mum and Dad my discovery. With careful manoeuvring

I carried the needlework box through the hatch, down the stairs and, pushing the door open with my foot, into the lounge where my parents were still sorting through their books.

"Look what I found," I announced, with a grin.

Mum gasped. "Good heavens. I'd completely forgotten about that!"

I put the box down and noticed Dad's eyes travel over it as Mum sat on a chair and lifted the lid.

"Be careful," I said. But it was too late. The lid came away in her hands.

She looked up at Dad and narrowed her eyes. "You were supposed to repair this, remember? Sharon knocked a glass of water over it when she was a kiddie. Then the hinges went. In the end I got fed up asking you to sort it out."

"In case you've forgotten, we lived in a tiny flat where there was no outside space for me to sand it down, and by the time we moved here I was working all the hours under the sun. Besides, neither of us had even remembered it was in the loft until now," Dad replied.

Mum sighed and gazed at the lid on her lap. "True. We're both guilty of neglecting it."

"Was it always your box?" I asked.

She looked at me as though I had two heads. "Of course. Your father made it for me when first started courting."

"That's right. I wanted to impress her in those days," he said.

I frowned and ran my hand across the pattern. "But what about these initials?"

"They stand for your Mum and me," Dad said, proudly. "SAR. Susan And Robert. It was your mum who started to call me →

Bobby a little while later, after she got sweet on me."

He winked at her and she returned a shy half smile.

"I spent hours in my father's shed, French polishing the wood and fitting shiny brass hinges." He sighed. "But gradually, over the years, it started to fall apart."

"It can be repaired, Dad," I said, giving him a hug. "It just needs a bit of time and effort. Things don't stay pristine forever."

I turned to Mum and told her, "Look under the tray."

said, putting his arm around Mum's shoulders and kissing the top of her head.

It was such an unusual display of affection I felt my throat squeeze.

I gave a little cough. "Well, I think I'll call it a day. Tim and I will be over at the weekend and Holly and Abby will have fun helping sort through the rest of the loft."

Mum nodded as she eased herself up from the chair.

"You know what? I might not be able to stand and bake like I used to, but I can still make a decent outfit when I put my

Dad put his arm around Mum's shoulders and kissed the top of her head

She put the lid on the floor. "Would you believe it?" she said, taking out the newspaper. I thought I'd thrown this out by mistake years ago!"

She turned to the middle pages. Dad looked over her shoulder. "We were a handsome couple in those days, weren't we?" he said, with a break in his voice.

Mum nodded. "A happy ever after," she read out, wistfully, looking up at Dad. "That feels a long way off at the moment."

"This is all mini drama, nothing more," I said. "You'll be fine once your moved."

"And the story's not over yet," Dad

mind to it. Blow the old recipe books."

"And I never was much of a fisherman. Woodwork was more my cup of tea," Dad said, with a smile. "And once we've moved, that box will be my first project in my new shed."

"Thanks for your help, love," Mum said, when she and Dad kissed me goodbye.

Their marriage never was a fairy-tale. To be honest, real life rarely is. But in the next chapter of their lives, I have an idea that an old needlework box will have worked some magic. 🅜🅦

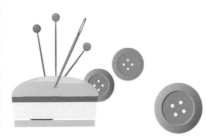

* * * * * * * * * *

THE FIRST BOOK I READ...

I remember reading *Heidi* when I was about seven. The story of the little orphan girl living in the Swiss mountains with her grandfather taught me about the importance of kindness and friendship.

Brain Boosters

Missing Link

The answer to each clue is a word which has a link with each of the three words listed.
This word may come at the end (eg **HEAD** linked with **BEACH**, **BIG**, **HAMMER**), at the beginning (eg **BLACK** linked with **BEAUTY**, **BOARD** and **JACK**) or a mixture of the two (eg **STONE** linked with **HAIL**, **LIME** and **WALL**).

ACROSS

1 Bird, Mat, Tub (4)
3 Gravity, Heat, Performance (8)
8 Beef, Fire, Man (5)
9 Board, Match, Men (5)
11 Nut, Tea, Treasure (5)
12 Chasing, Church, Jack (7)
14 Blue, Bright, Down (4)
16 Cloud, Pin, Teen (4)
20 Cloud, Storm, Struck (7)
22 Black, Cricket, Fork (5)
24 Fat, Hush, Love (5)
26 Book, Line, Tour (5)
27 Become, Heir, Magnitude (8)
28 Eleven, Fore, Sea (4)

DOWN

1 Library, Line, Olive (6)
2 Park, Pub, Tune (5)
4 Book, Catch, Para (6)
5 Helmet, Life, Motor (5)
6 Entrance, Membership, Transfer (3)
7 Balkan, Federal, United (6)
10 Mustard, Poppy, Pumpkin (4)
13 Chip, Dust, Pipes (3)
15 After, Bet, Thank (3)
16 Paper, Ring, Table (6)
17 Bus, Full, Gap (4)
18 Fly, Komodo, Snap (6)
19 Dawn, Girl, Line (6)
21 Blow, Hair, Tumble (5)
23 All, Fore, Upon (5)
25 Pill, Talk, Up (3)

Turn To Page 165 For Solutions

Hidden word in the shaded squares: _____

Gone Girl

Nothing evokes the spirit of a teenager quite like the mess they leave behind them…

By Karen Wane

Rachel opened the door of Libby's bedroom and turned on the light. It was just as she had left it. An unmade bed. An empty plate with toast crumbs lay on the floor, not even placed on the bedside table.

Not that there was any room on it anyway. Along with dozens of bits of cheap jewellery there were several bottles of nail polish, many with their tops still half off. It looked as if she had been in a real hurry to get away.

To say the room looked as if a bomb had hit it was an understatement. Clothes were strewn everywhere. Discarded

herself up with the sniffles or a nasty cough. Those moments when she had awoken from a bad dream.

Rachel or Mike – usually Rachel – would have lifted her out of her cot, which in no time at all became a big bed, and cuddled her on the chair trying to make it all better. Where had the time gone? Rachel wondered. She picked up one of the T-shirts to wipe away the tears on her cheek.

Time to start tidying all this mess up. But where to start? And did she even want to? Leaving the room how Libby had left it meant she could come in and remember her just as she was – an untidy,

Rachel attempted to sit the toys up straight, to smooth their matted hair

dresses dangling over the wardrobe doors had slipped off their hangers onto the floor. The comfy wing-backed chair in the corner of the room could hardly be seen under a layer of T-shirts.

Rachel moved them onto the bed in order to sit down. The chair had been new eighteen years ago when Libby had been born. The memories came flooding back. How she had sat there nursing her as a baby. The times when she had held her when she couldn't sleep and had woken

messy teenager. Making it all neat and tidy. That was how Rachel was, not Libby, and she didn't feel ready to remove all traces of her daughter just yet.

Rachel looked around the room and found that Libby's cuddly toy collection was still intact at the bottom of the bed. Her favourite, the one-eyed bear with the red bow tie, was half hidden underneath the massive furry My Little Pony her auntie had bought her when she was seven. When asked why she had named the bear Brownie, the three-year-old Libby had replied, "Because he's brown."

Then there was the time when four-year-old Libby had been distraught when Rachel tried to sew him another eye on.

"You'll hurt him, Mummy!" she had cried. So Brownie had remained with only one eye ever since.

Sitting on a set of drawers was her doll collection. All had connections to the films she had loved as a child. There was Ariel, the Little Mermaid, Belle from *Beauty and the Beast*, Jasmine (Aladdin's love interest) alongside Pocahontas. The videos had to be watched over and over again. Libby had been bought all the costumes too. She had always loved dressing up.

Rachel thought of Libby twirling around in her yellow crinoline as Belle and trying to fix her bright red wig on when she wanted to be the Little Mermaid in a fancy dress competition.

How Libby had squealed with delight when Mike had pulled her round the kitchen floor while sitting on a rug pretending to be Jasmine riding on the flying carpet.

"Again, Daddy, again!" she begged.

Now Rachel attempted to sit the dolls up neatly and settle their matted hair into place. They were all looking a bit forlorn. Rather like Rachel now. Why didn't anyone else understand?

She'd heard enough of "You'll soon ➡

have the house to yourselves. Lucky you."
(Mrs Firth from next door.)

"Bet you'll be glad to get her off your hands." (Mrs Tilley from over the road.)

Rachel had always wanted a girl. After so many difficult pregnancies ending with nothing, she had been thrilled when her wish had come true.

She and Libby had shared a similar temperament and had always got on well. Apart from one or two teenage tantrums over the years, they were extremely close and loved nothing more than a girly day out shopping or visiting a beauty salon.

Rachel had actively encouraged her daughter to reach for the stars. Hadn't she named her Liberty? She had wanted her to experience the freedom and independence Rachel never had, growing up in a small market town in the seventies.

Vivacious Libby had always grasped life with both hands. She felt so empty without her. Were things ever going to be the same again?

ILLUSTRATIONS: ISTOCKPHOTO, REX/SHUTTERSTOCK

Rachel switched the light off and closed the bedroom door. Slowly she went downstairs and into the kitchen where Mike was making her a cup of tea. He put his arms around her, trying to make her feel better.

"Let's do something different. We could go away for the weekend," he suggested.

"Could do," Rachel answered quietly. "Where shall we go?"

Just then, Rachel's phone rang. Libby!

"Hi Mum." Rachel's face lit up at hearing from her daughter so soon. After all, it had only been a few days since they had dropped her off at university even though it felt like a lifetime

"I've forgotten to bring Brownie. Could you bring him down to me at the weekend, please? Besides, I'm dying to show you the new posters I've bought for my room." Then she added, "And by the way, I started to write you a card before I went, but I couldn't find the right words. I want you to know I miss you."

"Brownie's missed you too," replied Rachel softly.

Putting down the phone, she turned to Mike questioningly.

"How do you feel about going to Exeter for the weekend?"

"Can't think of anywhere nicer," said Mike with a smile. Ⓜ

THE FIRST BOOK I READ...

I remember reading *Little Women* aged around 10. Having two older brothers myself, I always wished I had had sisters and I most definitely wanted to be Jo March.

✦ Your nose gets used to scents quickly, so if you can smell it yourself, your colleagues will be positively wilting!

✦ That perfume you love on your best friend will not smell the same on you due to genetic differences in skin's chemistry interacting with perfumes to change its base scent.

✦ Science has proved a connection between smell and emotions, so the right scent really will make you feel better. Try lavender for relaxation, or citrus to give an instant energy boost.

✦ After you spray perfume, do NOT rub it in – the friction distorts the scent. Dab if you must, but it's even better to just let it be – it will last longer.

✦ Coco Chanel came from humble beginnings – her mother was a laundry woman. Chanel No 5 was her first perfume, and also the first to be made with a synthetic aldehyde that smelled of – yes, soap.

FANCY THAT!

Fascinating facts on **Perfume!**

✦ The most expensive perfume in the world is Clive Christian's Imperial Majesty at $215,000 for 16.9 ounces, in a Baccarat crystal bottle with 18-carat gold and five-carat diamond collar.

✦ 84% of people will have memories that are triggered by a smell.

✦ Don't use Calvin Klein's Obsession if you're on safari as cheetahs, tigers and jaguars are attracted by the scent!

✦ Don't display beautiful perfume bottles until they're empty – scent should be stored, like wine, somewhere cool and dark.

It takes 8,000lbs of rose petals to produce 2.2lbs of rose absolute

✦ Jean Carles, the famed French perfumer who created scents such as Miss Dior, was said to have insured his nose for a million dollars.

✦ The earliest perfumes were created by burning spices and herbs such as frankincense – hence the name "per fume" which is Latin for "through smoke".

✦ Jasmine notes in some fragrances are produced by using a synthetic material derived from – wait for it – coal tar!

WORDS: BABS BEATON PICTURES: ISTOCKPHOTO, REX/SHUTTERSTOCK

Sealed With A Kiss?

Joy, sorrow, hope and new beginnings – so many emotions bound up with a humble postbox

By Kate Finnemore

Conscious of the smile that lit her face, Matilda threaded her way between the groups of people crowding round the new postbox. Every now and then she danced a step or two. She held her hands to her chest, the left hand on top of the right, not so much to keep the letter she was going to post safe, but rather so that everyone could see – and admire – her ring.

Her engagement ring. She didn't normally show off like this, she wasn't that sort. But ever since the Sunday before, she simply couldn't help it. Her Ned had asked her to be his wife, and she was so happy, she was bubbling over

and women, some of them holding letters of their own, turned to face the front, children stopped their games and stood still, and Sir Lionel began his speech.

"This is indeed a momentous occasion. Modern times have at last reached Westcote. At last we have our very own postbox. No longer will we be obliged to travel to Northcote to post our letters."

He paused, interrupted by a burst of clapping, before going on, "It's been twenty-five years since our gracious Queen Victoria ascended the throne, and in that time –"

"You look very happy, my dear."

The quiet woman's voice startled Matilda. She looked round, and saw to her consternation that Lady Westcote

She ought to bring up the subject of the ring, but was unsure how to phrase it

with it – and she wanted everyone to share her happiness with her.

She was now close to the front of the crowd, near where Sir Lionel, Lady Westcote and their young son stood beside the postbox newly installed in the short stretch of wall between the church and the bakery. It gleamed bright red in the June sunshine.

Sir Lionel noisily cleared his throat and the buzz of conversation died down. Men

had come to stand beside her.

"I am, my lady," she said, bobbing a curtsey. She lowered her eyes, knowing she ought to bring up the subject of the ring, but unsure how to phrase it.

"Your Ned is a brave man," Lady Westcote said. "He saved my beloved son's life. If Ned hadn't swum out to him, my son would have drowned."

"Yes, my lady." Matilda ran her tongue across her lips. "I –" ➡

"No, don't thank me for it. The ring is a token of my immense gratitude to him. If it has enabled him to propose to you in due style, then that is an extra blessing. It looks very good on you, my dear."

Relieved that the subject was out in the open, Matilda held her hand out, palm down. It was the most beautiful ring ever, she thought, happiness bubbling up again – a circle of tiny diamonds surrounding a sapphire the rich deep blue of her eyes.

"I – uh, thank you, my lady." There was a breathless catch in her voice.

"And Sir Lionel has given Ned a sum of money to help him set up a shop here in the village."

"That's what he's always wanted to do, my lady."

"He deserves to have his dream come true." Lady Westcote patted Matilda's arm. "I wish the two of you every happiness."

"Thank you, my lady."

Matilda watched as Lady Westcote turned, full skirts swaying, to rejoin her husband.

"And finally," he was saying, "the time has come to designate the person who

heady, wonderful thought.

He was working in Northcote. It wasn't far. She could have walked over and saved herself the penny for the stamp. But she hadn't, and it occurred to her that her love for Ned would always, somehow, be connected to this postbox.

She recalled the last words she'd written the night before: *I shall treasure your ring always, my dearest Ned, just as I shall always treasure your love for me.* Then she'd folded the single sheet of paper, sealed it with two blobs of wax, and stuck the stamp on the outside.

Now, with a shy glance at the people all around, she touched a kiss to her letter and smiled. She pushed it into the postbox, sending on their way her heartfelt words to the man she loved.

Clarisse Watson paced up and down the pavement by Westcote's postbox. In her hands was a box wrapped in brown paper tied round with string. It was small enough to go through the slot, she could see that every time she held it out towards the postbox. Just one tiny push and the

But she couldn't do it. Again she turned away, pulling up the collar of her coat

will have the honour of being the first to post a letter in this splendid new box. We have drawn lots, and the winner is – young Matilda here."

A fresh burst of cheering and clapping greeted the announcement. Matilda felt her cheeks burn red. Someone behind her pushed her gently forward with a low "Go on, Matty dear."

Blushing, she stood next to the postbox, and held her letter to her lips. It was a love letter, of course, to her dearest Ned. Ned Blakeney. And this time next year she would be Mrs Ned Blakeney. It was a

deed would be done, she told herself.

But she couldn't do it. Again she turned away, pulling the collar of her coat up to her ears. It was dark still, though the sky was lightening in the east, and the rain had started in earnest. She'd been too agitated to think of bringing her umbrella, and was grateful for the cloche hat she wore.

Was she doing the right thing? The box contained the ring George Blakeney had given her on their engagement, a beautiful sapphire set within a circle of sparkling diamonds. George had told her how his grandfather had been given it as a reward.

He'd dived into the lake and rescued the present occupant of Westcote House, then a young boy, who'd fallen out of a boat. George's grandmother had worn the ring every day of her long and happy marriage to his grandfather.

Would her marriage to George be as happy? She'd never – well, almost never – doubted it. Until the evening before.

Tears filled Clarisse's eyes as she relived the scene she'd witnessed.

She'd written to George later that night.

I'm crying as I write this. I love you so much, George. I still do. I feel as if my heart is breaking. Writing this letter, returning your ring, it's the hardest thing I've ever done. But I've got to do it. I've thought about it, over and over, but I just can't forgive you for what you've done.

You've betrayed me. You really have, George, and I suspect it's not the first time. How can I ever trust you again?

Clarisse recalled how she'd walked into Blakeney's General Stores, the shop George's grandfather had started decades before. George's parents and George himself now ran it. It was almost closing time and the shop was empty. His parents must have already headed upstairs as they usually did around five o'clock. But where was George?

Sounds from the store room at the back, and muffled voices, gave Clarisse her answer. Her heart leapt. A smile lit up her face, and she swiftly crossed the shop, pulled aside the curtain – and then she jerked to a halt.

George was there. Together with Esme Dodd, one of the maids at Westcote House. They stood very close. And it was clear that only seconds before they'd been much closer. Esme's lips had a bruised look to them, and there was a smudge of her lipstick on George's mouth.

Clarisse's hands clenched, nails biting into her palms. Tears filled her eyes. But she wouldn't cry, she told herself. Not yet.

"Don't say anything, George." Only the quiver in her voice betrayed her hurt. "There's nothing you can say to explain."

With that she turned, walked back across the shop and out of the door.

Arriving home, unable to face her parents, she ran straight upstairs to her room and threw herself down on the bed. The tears came then, stinging tears of pain and lost love, and anger with herself. How blind she'd been. His brother had hinted on more than one occasion that George had an eye for the ladies. But she'd told herself he was so handsome, such a charmer, it was no wonder young women threw themselves at him. What a fool she was.

Much later, in the small hours of the night, she'd got up from her bed, taken out paper, pen and ink and written her letter. Then she'd twisted her engagement ring off her finger, placed it in its box and folded ➤

the letter round it.

It was almost dawn. The postman would arrive soon for the six o'clock collection. Clarisse knew what she had to do.

So why was she hesitating?

Because she should simply forgive him? That's what women did, wasn't it? Besides, they were engaged, not married. George hadn't made any formal vows to her as yet.

Or was it because the war had taken so many young men, and she was afraid of being left on the shelf?

No, it was far simpler than that. She'd said it in her letter. She could never trust him again, and without trust there could be no marriage.

All at once all doubt had gone. Squaring her shoulders, Clarisse stepped forward and pushed the small parcel into the postbox. She heard the sound – a very final sound – as it dropped to the bottom, and turned away.

Vera Blakeney pulled the cap off her fountain pen, drew the pad of flimsy writing paper nearer, and started to write.

Westcote, 23rd March 1942
Dearest Philip,

I hope you are well, pet. I know you can't tell me anything about the fighting or how the war's going, but I do worry about you. You're in my thoughts all the time, dearest, and every time I think of you I kiss the beautiful sapphire ring you gave me on our engagement, and the wedding band that still seems so bright and shiny and new. Only a year, we've only been married a year. It doesn't seem possible, does it?

Ouch, Master (or Miss) Bump has just given me an almighty kick! I wonder if it'll be a boy or a girl. I know you say you Blakeneys only ever produce boys, but a girl would be nice, don't you think?

Africa seems so far away. Every now and then I walk over to the library in Northcote and look at a map of Africa in the atlas. So far away and so big. I imagine you there, in the desert, having to fight in the heat and the dust, and I can't bear to think of it, pet.

Your dear Uncle George is still running the shop and doing a good job of it. There's something very sad about him, I always think. Even though it was so many years ago, what happened between him and Clarisse Watson still tears him up. He says over and over that he threw away his one true chance of happiness by his own stupidity. It's a pity he never found someone else who might have made him happy.

I go in and help as much as I can, though Master (or Miss!) Bump makes me very tired. Only three months to go! We have some strange things in the shop now – that American sausage meat for example, Spam they call it. No one was buying it, so they reduced the number of points you needed to buy it and it's going like hot cakes now! Gas and electricity have just gone on the rationed list. Oh, and Dolly next door is convinced the butcher in Northcote is selling cats, not rabbits. They've always had their ears cut off – that's how she knows, she says.

I know for sure, dear, that you didn't receive my last letter. Let me explain how I can be so certain: it wasn't a bomb, it was too small for that, and it didn't explode. But something – a piece of broken-up aeroplane perhaps – dropped out of the sky, landed right by the postbox and bounced up again, straight through the slot! A freak accident, everyone says. It must have been very hot because the letters inside started smouldering.

Uncle George was in the shop and

saw the smoke coming out of the slot. He couldn't open the box, of course, but he filled a teapot with water, would you believe, rushed over and poured it into the box while your Dad cycled into Northcote to tell the people at the post office. The end result was a pile of badly charred, sopping wet, illegible letters. The GPO man said the only thing to do was to destroy them!

So you won't receive yesterday's letter but you will receive this one, I hope, and know that I'm thinking of you always, my dearest.

Tears, as always, weren't far away as Vera read her letter through again, signed it and put it in an envelope. It was a lovely spring day, she thought. She'd walk down to the postbox and send it on its way.

Stephen should have been a doctor rather than an engineer, Vera thought, not for the first time, smiling as she sat down at the kitchen table and took her son's letter – a single sheet of almost illegible scrawl – out of the pale blue airmail envelope. She had plenty of time

me. She wants to stay here, all her family are here, so I asked my boss to extend my contract and he agreed. He's made it permanent.

Vera couldn't read any more. She felt cold all over. All at once her hand seemed to have no strength. It let both letter and photo drop back to the table.

It had happened. What she'd feared had happened.

If only Philip were here with her now, so that the two of them could talk it through. But he was out and about for the day, researching new lines for the shop.

She ought to be glad for her son, her only child. He had a good job, a very good job, and now he'd met someone he wanted to settle down with. No doubt they'd have children. She'd be a grandmother.

She wanted to be happy for him, for them both. But it was so difficult. He was in Sydney. In Australia. It was the other side of the world. If Stephen settled in Australia, she'd never see him again! She'd never get to know his wife. She'd never play with the grandchildren.

She looked very nice, Vera thought, and then felt the first stirrings of unease

– she didn't have to open the shop for another half hour.

There was a colour photo too: Stephen, so like his father, tall, with thick dark hair and those stunning sapphire-blue eyes. He had put his arm round the shoulders of the young woman at his side, drawing her to him. Vera saw long sun-bleached hair, golden skin with a spattering of freckles across the nose, and a wide smile. She looked very nice, Vera thought, and felt the first stirrings of unease.

She turned her attention to the letter.
I've met a girl, Mum. Her name's Robyn. I'm going to ask her to marry

Never read them bedtime stories.

Somehow, she managed to get through the day, putting on a cheerful face as she served her customers, though several remarked that she seemed distracted.

By the time Phil came home and they sat down for their evening meal, she had made a few decisions.

"I'm sure George would love to come out of retirement, pet," she said, "and take charge in the shop for a while. So how about I cycle over to the travel agent's in Northcote tomorrow and find out how much it'll cost to travel to Australia?" ➤

"Hmm." Phil speared a potato with his fork. "A return trip by boat'll take two months, plus a month over there. We'll be away for three months. George might not fancy being tied to the shop for so long."

"Well, jet aeroplane, then. Though it'll cost an arm and a leg. We might not be able to save up enough in time for the wedding."

"Maybe not, but we'll try our best."

Vera looked up, startled, as Philip covered her hand with his. She saw his quiet determination, and his concern for her in his expression, and her heart gave

of the last (maybe even the very last!) to be sent from it.

People aren't writing so many letters now, the GPO says. They're using the telephone instead. It feels like the end of an era, and the start of a new one, an era of telephones and jet planes – and the start of a long, happy, settled life for you, my dear son, in Australia.

She'd pop out and post the letter in a while, she decided, folding the four sheets of airmail paper and sliding them into the envelope. And tomorrow she'd take the small parcel to the post office in Northcote,

For a moment she simply held it, running her fingertips across the sapphire

a little jolt. The war years and post-war austerity had left their marks on his face, and his hair was now threaded with silver at the temples. But she still loved him as much as she ever had.

"There's something else." Vera hesitated. "My engagement ring. It's brought a long and happy marriage to the two women who've worn it, your great-grandmother and me. So I was thinking –"

"Yes."

It was a statement, not a question.

Vera laughed nervously.

"Phil, you don't even know what I'm going to say!"

"Yes, I do. And I agree."

The postbox here in Westcote, Vera wrote later that evening, nearing the end of a long letter to her son, *is due to be decommissioned tomorrow. It'll be sealed and painted black. This letter will be one*

have it weighed and sent to her son by registered post. She had the box, the brown paper and the sticky tape ready. Now was the time.

She looked across at Philip, sitting on the other side of the table, as she eased her engagement ring off her finger. For a moment she simply held it, running her fingertips across the sparkling sapphire. Then, touching it to her lips, she put it into its box and tucked the briefest of notes in beside it:

With all my love, Mum.

. . . .

THE FIRST BOOK I READ...

Not a novel but a collection of short stories: Rudyard Kipling's *Just So Stories*. I must have been about six, and found them funny, exotic – and totally enthralling.

Snowman Pops

Ingredients (Makes 8)

- **100g plain cake crumbs**
- **50g vanilla frosting**
- **50g icing sugar**
- **8 mini plain ring doughnuts**
- **White and chocolate piping icing and small chocolate beans, to decorate**

1 Put the cake crumbs in a bowl and mix in the frosting to form a firm mixture. Divide into 8 and form each into a ball. Place on a plate, cover and chill for 30min.

2 Just before serving, line a board with baking parchment. Sift the icing sugar into a bowl. Working on 1 pop at a time, toss a cake ball and a mini doughnut in the sugar until well coated then thread on to a wooden skewer. Lay them on the board while you prepare the others.

3 Brush away a little icing sugar to enable you to pipe on the decoration, and stick on chocolate beans. Do the same for the features. Best served as soon as possible after making.

The Mystery Shopper

Who was the helpful but elusive Barry? Jan was determined to find out the truth behind the mystery!

By Della Galton

Jan glanced up from her checkout as her customer put out the last of her shopping. It had been another busy day. They were short staffed as usual. She supposed there were bound to be teething problems – the store had only been open a fortnight – but it was beginning to wear her down.

Forcing a smile she glanced up to welcome her customer and saw to her surprise that she was smiling too.

"Next time you speak to your manager, could you pass on my congratulations," she said, her eyes twinkling.

"Your congratulations… um… yes, of course… what for?"

"You've a gentleman called Barry who is lovely. I couldn't find the cooking wine or the rock salt and he directed me to the right place. Lovely manners – and so kind. You should get more like him."

"Right," said Jan, racking her brains to think who Barry was. "Well, thank you. I'll pass that on."

On her break she was chatting to one of the other cashiers and Barry's name came up again.

"He showed an old guy where his favourite kind of shaving brushes were – the chap was ever so pleased. I didn't even know we sold shaving brushes."

"I didn't know we had a Barry," Jan confessed. "Apparently he's a dab hand at finding cooking wine and rock salt too."

She forgot all about Barry until the next team meeting when his name came up yet again.

"A customer told me he ought to get a pay rise," one of the teenagers who did shelf filling remarked. "Who is he anyway? I've never seen anyone called Barry."

The manager consulted her list. "That's

because we don't have a Barry. How very odd. She glanced at the only two men present, Jack and Tony. "It's not one of you guys messing about, is it?"

They both shook their heads and looked puzzled. "Why would we do that?"

"Does anyone know what he actually looks like?" she went on, tapping her pen against her clipboard.

"Older guy apparently with a moustache and grey hair," someone said. "Anyone working here who looks like that?"

"Not as far as I know," said the manager, pursing her lips. "Keep your eyes peeled, everyone – maybe it's a customer impersonating a member of staff. That's a little worrying."

Jan supposed it was worrying. On the other hand this Barry didn't seem to be upsetting anyone – far from it. He was making their lives easier. If he wasn't even on the payroll what harm could it do?

On Sunday she cooked a roast for her parents as usual and Mum asked how she was getting on with her new job. "Have they got their staffing levels sorted out yet, love?"

Jan told her about Barry.

"Not that he's actually on the staff," she said. "But he certainly gets the most compliments."

"What does he look like?" Mum asked.

Jan told her and she gave a ➡

Even if he wasn't on the payroll, what harm was he doing helping customers?

thoughtful frown. "Sounds like the guy who used to work in the corner shop. I'm not sure of his name was but he had grey hair and a moustache, about the right age."

"What corner shop was that?"

"The one that was in the parade of shops they knocked down to build that supermarket."

"Really?" Jan frowned. "How intriguing. Well, maybe it is him. Maybe he still wants to keep his hand in, so he pops in now and then to see what's what."

"Or maybe he's a ghost." Mum widened her eyes in glee. "Maybe he died of a broken heart when they took away his shop. It had been in his family for generations, hadn't it, love?" She glanced at Jan's father. "What was the name of that place? Simpson & Son?"

"Gibson and Son." Dad nodded thoughtfully. "Nice old fellow, Mr Gibson. I used to get my paper in there. And

She was just passing the deli section when she spotted a grey haired man up ahead. He had his back to her and was talking to someone so she couldn't see if he had a moustache. She felt a shiver pass across her shoulder blades, although that could have been the cool air wafting out of the chiller units.

"Hey," she called, as she got closer and both customers turned towards her. The grey haired man did not have a moustache, to her disappointment. And he was clearly with his wife. They were poring over a shopping list.

"Is everything all right?" she improvised hastily. "Can I help you with anything?"

"Thanks, love, but we're fine," the woman said with a smile. "We were a bit stuck for the batter mix earlier, but a very nice gentleman by the name of Barry pointed us in the right direction."

She spun round and the man who'd been standing beside her had just vanished

you're absolutely right – he didn't want to sell up. He was pretty fed up about it from what I remember."

"There you go." Mum said, fascinated. She loved all things supernatural. "You've got a ghostly check-out operator. Oooh, I think I might pop by."

"He's not on the check out," Jan said with a nervous laugh. She wasn't sure she liked the idea of a ghostly member of staff moving among them. However helpful he was. Not that she was quite such a believer as Mum was.

Never the less, next time she was at work she decided to do a spot of research. During the mid afternoon lull she closed her check out and took a little wander around the store.

"I don't suppose you could tell me where he went," Jan said.

"Didn't really notice, love, sorry."

"He just disappeared," the man added. "One minute there and the next gone…"

Frustrated, Jan thanked them. So close, but yet so far.

It was as she was serving later that afternoon that the solution hit her. Everyone who'd seen the mysterious Barry had been looking for something. So surely if she did the same, he might appear.

She needed some shopping anyway. So when she finished her shift, she took off her badge, grabbed a basket and headed down the first aisle.

She was half way through her purchases when she realised that she actually couldn't find the custard powder.

How did this work? Did she have to say it out loud? She drum-rolled her fingers on the handle of her basket. "Now where, oh where, is the custard powder?"

She had barely finished the sentence when he appeared beside her. A grey haired man with a moustache and a friendly smile – and yes, there on his badge, identical to the one she'd been wearing earlier, was the name Barry.

"Can I help you with something, love?"

She stared at him in disbelief. Was there a faint shimmer around the outline of his uniform or was it her imagination?

"Custard powder, was it?"

"Um… yes. Please."

Gosh, she hadn't planned any further than this. How did you ask someone if they were a ghost? You could hardly just come out with it. Perhaps she should engineer a way of touching him. Ghosts didn't have any substance, did they? Mind you, that was easier said than done. He was walking a little way ahead of her and when she tried to catch up, it seemed he upped his pace too, so she never actually got any closer. Then, suddenly he paused, and she realised with dismay they were at the custard powder.

"There you go, sweetheart."

It was now or never. She leaned in to touch him, but at the precise moment her fingers were about to make contact she heard a yell behind her.

"Jan! Quick!"

She glanced over her shoulder just in time to see Megan, one of the teenagers, hurrying towards her.

"I think I've just seen him. Barry, I mean. He's in aisle three. He just showed a woman where the cat food was."

"He can't have done – he's here."

She spun round again to see… nothing. The man who'd been standing beside her, had vanished.

So have you got any closer to finding out the identity of the mysterious Barry?" Mum asked, next time they met up for lunch.

"Not really," Jan said, "Although I did meet him the other day." She explained what had happened and her parents listened with interest.

"I'm beginning to think that your ghost theory might be right," she said. "And I have a plan."

"What plan?" her father asked.

"If I told you I'd have to kill you! Watch this space…"

Actually the truth of the matter was that Jan didn't exactly know what she was going to do. But she was sure that the answer to the mystery lay with the ➜

old shopkeeper, Mr Gibson. She was determined to track him down. Which was trickier than she'd thought.

He seemed to have disappeared without a trace. In books it took half an hour on the Internet to find someone; in real life it took her a week. Even then she didn't find his address, but she found his son's. His son's name was Steve and Jan decided the best thing to do would be to call round and see him.

Steve opened the door with a frown and when she explained who she was, he stopped her.

"So you're really after my dad?" he said, his frowning.

Jan nodded and held her breath. He looked so serious that for a breathless moment she thought he was going to say his father had passed away.

"He's here having a spot of supper." He shouted back over his shoulder. "Dad, there's a woman here wants to see you."

Mr Gibson senior did look a bit like Barry, Jan saw, as he appeared. But he was slightly thinner and had different colour eyes and introduced himself as Tim. He shook her warmly by the hand.

"Good to meet you. Did you say you're the manager of Fine Foods?"

"No, I'm just a checkout girl," she said, wondering where to go from here. She couldn't exactly just come out with it and say she had thought he was dead and that his ghost was wandering about the supermarket! Luckily he seemed happy to do all the talking.

"I do miss my little shop," he said. "Although I'm enjoying my retirement." He paused. "When the developers first came sniffing about I must say I was none too happy."

"No," Jan said, "I'm not surprised."

"I wasn't ready to retire, see. I was happy working. I was OK in the end though. I kind of accepted things – and they did make it worth my while." He frowned. "In fact towards the end the developer and I got on quite well. We had this running argument going. Who provides the best customer service – corner shops or supermarkets? Well naturally I thought it was corner shops and he thought it was supermarkets."

"Naturally," Jan said.

He smiled. "I quite liked the fellow actually. Despite him being such a stubborn beggar. Kept saying to me, I'll show you what good customer service is. You come into Fine Foods when it's done. Come as a mystery shopper – you don't have to announce yourself. But I guarantee you'll get excellent service. Just as good as what you'd have given."

"And have you ever been?" Jan said.

"Not yet. I've been busy with the grandkids since I retired. Also, I did hear a rumour that he'd had a heart attack and died." He looked at her keenly. "Would you know if that was true?

"I might go over some time," he went on. "I can still remember the last conversation we had. He said he'd prove me wrong about who provided the best customer service. I said he couldn't prove me wrong if he had all eternity to do it." He chuckled. "Barry, his name was. I'd love to know what happened to him."

"Oh! I think I might be able to help after all…" Jan said. (MW)

Brain Boosters

Sudoku 1   Sudoku 2

Fill in each of the blank squares with the numbers 1 to 9, so that each row, each column and each 3x3 cell contains all the numbers from 1 to 9.

Sudoku 1

		4						
	5		7	2	3			
6	7		8			9		
7	4						9	
				3			8	
	1	5	9			3	7	
		2	1					7
		2		8	4	1		
				4	8			

Sudoku 2

			7	8	5			9
						1		7
		5		7	3		8	
4					5		1	
5						8		
3				1			6	
	9			4	8		7	
						6		5
		4	5	6			2	

Word Wheel

Turn To Page 165 For Solutions

You have ten minutes to find as many words as possible using the letters in the wheel. Each word must be three letters or more and contain the central letter. Use each letter once and no plurals, foreign words or porper nouns are allowed. There is at least one nine-letter word.

Letters: R, A, D, E, P, R, I, T with central G

Average: 30 words
Good: 31-45 words
Excellent: 46-60 words

The Rocket

Ben buys fireworks to try to cheer her up… could their little display of light be a good omen for the future?

By Pat Holness

"You're popular today." Harry, our local postie grins as he hands me a wodge of mail.

"I hope it'll be good news this time." I smile as I take the letters from him. A freshly brewed cup of coffee is waiting on the worktop, so I perch on a kitchen stool, take a sip and open my mail.

"How was your day?" Ben asks when he comes in at tea time.

"Not a single interview offer."

Ben takes me in his arms and plants a kiss on the top of my head.

"Cheer up chicken. Something's bound to happen soon."

"It better had if we're to get a foot on the property ladder," I sigh.

Even my ever-positive partner has to agree we both need to be earning if we're ever to realise dreams of our own house.

"It looks like a winner to me!" We hug one another and laugh.

All the same, a fortnight later there's still no offer of a job interview.

"They're probably putting them in the waste paper bin," I remark half-jokingly.

"Or they're deciding that you're the one for the job." Even Ben doesn't sound so sure this time.

"Tell you what," he goes on, "it's Guy Fawkes in a couple of days. We could buy some fireworks to cheer ourselves up."

"Great idea, I say, "Blow the expense."

Next evening is the fourth of November, so we go shopping in our local store and purchase a small box of assorted fireworks.

"It's going to be a gas!" says Ben, excited as a mischievous kid.

"Oh, no!"

Ben comes running to see what's happened as I unpack the groceries in the

There's still no reply from my latest job application but I put it out of my mind

"Never mind." Ben has an infectious grin and I can't help but smile back, "I've brought home the new local rag. Scan through it and wop off another application while I peel the veg to go with that delicious-smelling casserole you've concocted."

I do as he suggests and we open a bottle of cheap plonk to go with supper. Afterwards Ben picks up my application envelope and peers at it.

kitchen. "The bottle of juice must have had a loose lid; it's spilled all over our fireworks!"

Suddenly it's all too much and I break down in tears.

"Hey!" Ben holds me close. "We can still have our display. The fireworks are bound to have dried out by tomorrow evening. We won't splash out on another box, but the least I can do is treat us to another bottle of juice because that's the

kind of generous guy I am!"

I'm not so sure about the drying procedure, but I place the open box by a window and hope for the best. After all Guy Fawkes is still a day away.

The fifth of November dawns dry and remains so through the day. The box of fireworks looks OK so I hope for the best.

Ben goes to work and I scan the internet for more jobs. There's no reply from my latest application but I decide to put it out of my mind for the evening.

I make our favourite lasagne for supper and afterwards Ben peers out at the sky.

"All dry and fine," he says. "It's the perfect evening for fireworks. Will you please be so kind as to put on your coat and gloves and accompany me to the back yard, my darling?"

Taking the box and some matches outside, we sort out the fireworks.

"They're my favourites," I giggle as Ben poises a rocket in an empty bottle.

Ready, steady… go!" He sets light to the taper and stands back as the firework fizzles… and dies.

The next one, and the one after that, do exactly the same.

"I've one more rocket left." Ben's trying to sound cheerful, but suddenly the display seems to reflect our ambitions, somehow damp and listless.

He lights the final rocket and we wait as it hisses and begins to fizzle out.

Then, just as we're turning hand in hand to go indoors, the rocket comes to life, shoots into the sky and showers us with multi-coloured stars.

"Looks like a good omen to me," laughs Ben and we hug one another tight in the smoky darkness. Ⓜ

THE FIRST BOOK I READ…

The first novel I read was Alice in Wonderland when I was about eight. It inspired me to understand you can go anywhere in your imagination.

To The Moon And Back

There are some things in life that are just too tough to deal with on our own…

By Paula Williams

"You'll be very happy here, Charlie," the lady whose name Charlie couldn't remember said with a bright smile. "Mrs Marsh will look after you."

Charlie didn't expect he would be happy. He'd learned from a very early age not to expect much from life. That way, he wasn't disappointed when life – and the people who should have known better – let him down.

It started when his mum left him at Little Ducklings Day Care one rainy morning and didn't come back to collect him. There was a lot of whispering among the ladies at Little Ducklings and then this lady whose name he couldn't remember came and took him in her car to Mrs Marsh's house, where she said he'd be happy.

Charlie didn't expect he would be happy there. And, of course, he wasn't. Mrs Marsh was very kind. She smiled ➤

a lot and made him his favourite cheesy beans for tea. But he wanted to be back in his own bed. Not in this strange one, even though it had a stars and planets duvet cover and a picture of Thomas the Tank Engine on the wall.

Another lady came and asked him a lot of questions about where his mummy might be and where they lived. He knew it was up some stairs but they'd only lived there a few days and he couldn't remember where it was.

"Don't worry," the other lady said. "You and Mummy are new to the town. I expect she's got lost. We'll find her and tell her where you are then she'll come and take you home. I expect she's trying to find you right now."

Charlie decided not to say that he didn't think Mummy was trying to find him. She'd been very, very cross with him

very, very big trouble. The spotty china dog was Mummy's favourite thing in the whole wide world. She used to talk about it when she was in a good mood, and say how it reminded her of a spotty dog called Jemima that she used to have when she was a little girl. And then she would tell him stories of the things she and Jemima used to get up to.

Charlie loved those stories best of all. Better even than *Thomas the Tank Engine*.

But now, Mummy didn't have a china spotty dog any more because it broke into three pieces. And even though Charlie tried to fit the pieces back together – he was good at jigsaws – Mummy had snatched it away and threw it in the bin so hard that it broke into even more pieces.

"That's it, Charlie," she said in a funny voice he'd never heard before. It was all

The lady cried when she first saw him which Charlie thought was a bit rude

that morning. So cross, she didn't even kiss him goodbye when she dropped him off at Little Ducklings. Didn't say "Love you to the moon and back" and smooth his hair down like she usually did.

And it was all his fault. That morning, they were both late getting up and Mummy kept telling him to hurry. He'd been wriggling around when he was putting his jumper on because the sleeve had somehow got all tangled up and inside out. Then his arm had suddenly shot out and knocked the china spotty dog off the shelf and crashing to the floor.

That was when Charlie knew he was in

squeaky and a bit scary and didn't sound like her at all. "I can't do this any more." She walked about the kitchen, twisting her hands like she was cold. "I just can't cope. I'm sorry. I'm so, so sorry."

That was when she took him to Little Ducklings and forgot to kiss him goodbye and forgot to smooth down his hair and say "Love you to the moon and back". Because, Charlie thought, she probably didn't love him to the moon and back. Not any more.

He stayed at Mrs Marsh's house for quite a lot more days. He didn't know how many because he wasn't very good at counting yet. Only that it seemed a lot. And although he got to like this new bed with the stars and planets duvet cover and the picture of Thomas on the wall, it didn't feel like his bed.

While he was living at Mrs Marsh's house, lots of different people came and asked him lots of different questions. About him, about Mummy, about where they lived. They all smiled at him a lot and told him not to worry. One day they even took him out in a big blue car and drove him around the town to see if he saw anything he remembered.

But the only thing he remembered was the big supermarket where they sold broccoli which he hated and pinky squashy sweets which he loved but which Mummy said were bad for his teeth.

Then one day a lady came to Mrs Marsh's to see him. She had grey hair, a bright pink coat and seemed very nice, even though she cried when she first saw him which Charlie thought was a bit rude. But she said she was sorry she cried, that it was just because she was so pleased to see him. Which didn't seem rude any more. Just strange.

If he saw Mummy again, he'd be pleased to see her. But he wouldn't cry. He only cried when he hurt himself.

"Hello Charlie," the lady said.

Charlie nodded.

"I – I'm your grandmother."

Charlie wasn't sure what a grandmother was. Or if he wanted one. So he nodded again and looked down at his feet.

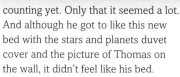

"I'm your mummy's mummy," she said quietly.

Charlie's head shot up.

"Is Mummy at your house?" he asked, his heart thumping.

But the lady shook her head and Charlie went back to looking at his feet.

"No, sweetheart," she said. "I don't know where Mummy is. But I'm sure she'll turn up. Very soon. In the meantime you're going to stay with Mrs Marsh for just a little longer while they sort a few things out. Then I'm hoping you'll come and stay with me. Just until Mummy comes back. If – if you'd like to, that is?"

Charlie didn't know whether he'd like to or not. But it didn't matter, because he didn't expect it would happen.

Jane held it together until she got back in the car. Then she put her head on the steering wheel and cried as if she was never going to stop.

That poor sweet little boy, looking up at her with Anna's eyes. Big, blue and so very, very wary. She'd wanted to snatch him up and take him home with her this minute. But rules were rules and she had to be patient while all the checks were made. She understood that.

But soon, she hoped, her four-year-long nightmare would be over. In part, at least. Four years since Anna had come to her that awful, awful night and blurted out that she was pregnant.

And what had she done? Only told the girl that it was her problem and that →

she'd have to deal with it. Even thinking about it now brought her out in a cold sweat. How could she have done that?

If only she could have turned the clock back to the moment just before she'd said, in that cold, dazed voice, "I've got enough problems of my own at the moment without taking on yours."

She hadn't meant it, of course. And she regretted it the moment the words had left her mouth.

But Anna hadn't waited for her apology or, indeed, for an explanation as to why her mother had suddenly acted so out of character. Instead, she'd stormed off.

If only Anna had waited, given her chance for her head to clear, she'd have calmed down and they'd have talked it through. Like they always used to do.

She could have explained how John, her husband of just eighteen months and Anna's stepfather, had just been diagnosed with throat cancer and Jane had spent twenty-four sleepless hours at the hospital, during which time her brain had turned to cotton wool. She was still reeling from the shock when Anna had made her announcement.

But Anna, impetuous as ever, hadn't waited. Instead, she'd stormed to her room, packed a couple of bags and disappeared from Jane's life.

She'd sent a brief text to say that she was living with the baby's father and she was doing OK.

After that, nothing. Not even when John died. And even though, on the day of his funeral, Jane had known it was a vain hope, still she looked for her daughter among the mourners. But, of course, she was not there.

Four long years of silence followed.

Jane had done everything she could to find her daughter, even hiring a private detective. But it seemed that Anna had simply disappeared off the face of the earth.

"Even these days," the detective told Jane, "it's hard to find someone who doesn't want to be found."

But then, two days ago, a letter had come in the post, in Anna's distinctive handwriting.

Jane took it out of her bag, but she didn't need to read it. Every word in that short note was already scored deeply into her brain.

Dear Mum, it said. *I know you probably don't ever want to see me again but I'm asking this not for me, but for Charlie. I've done a terrible thing and left him in care.*

I should have brought him to you but I was afraid you'd say no. And I had no one else. His father left before he was born, just like you said he would.

Please, please, please get in touch with Social Services on the number below. And tell Charlie (this was crossed out).

I'm a terrible mother. Don't try to find me, for Charlie's sake. He really is better off without me. I'm so sorry for all the trouble I've caused.

Jane re-folded the letter carefully, put it back into her bag and went home to prepare the house for her grandson who, according to the social worker, had still not spoken – except briefly to answer questions – and had become very withdrawn.

They were understandably concerned about him but hoped that, once back in a stable family environment that they were sure Jane would provide, Charlie would improve.

Jane hoped so, too. But she wasn't holding her breath.

Y ou'll be very happy here, Charlie," the lady whose name he couldn't remember said. "Your granny will look after you."

Charlie didn't expect he would be very happy. Since Mummy left, he wasn't very happy anywhere, even though Mrs Marsh was a very kind lady who smiled a lot and never made him eat broccoli or mushrooms. Sometimes, too, she even gave him pink squashy sweets.

He'd met his grandmother quite a few times now and she'd showed him how to play snakes and ladders and had taken him to the park and bought him an ice cream with a piece of chocolate in it.

"That picture was taken a long time ago and dogs don't live as long as humans, you know. But I've another spotty dog now and his name's Rocky. Would you like to meet him?

"He's longing to meet you. But only if you want to. You see, he's only a puppy and he gets very excited. He might jump at you. Do you like dogs, Charlie?"

Charlie liked dogs more than anything in the whole wide world. Except, of course, Mummy. He nodded.

"I love dogs, Granny," he said. "They're my favourite animals. And giraffes. They're my favourite too."

Granny laughed. "I don't have any giraffes, I'm afraid."

"Can I see Rocky now?" Charlie asked. He remembered what had happened to Mummy's china spotty dog and added,

Her house was bigger – and there were lots of pictures of Mummy in it

Her house was bigger than Mrs Marsh's. And there were lots of pictures of Mummy in it. One of them – the one he liked the best – was of Mummy with the spotty dog.

"That's Jemima," he said, speaking for the first time. Charlie didn't do a lot of talking. There was no point.

"Yes. It is." Granny was blinking hard again. Just like the first time they met.

"Is she here? In this house?"

Charlie's heart jumped in his throat, but sank back down again when Granny shook her head sadly.

"Jemima isn't here," Granny said.

"I won't break him, I promise."

"I'm more worried he'll break you, sweetheart." Granny laughed again.

She put her arm around Charlie's shoulders and hugged him. At one time he'd have pulled away. But now he quite liked it. She smelled of lemons and something sweet that reminded Charlie of his favourite biscuits.

"Come on then, Charlie. Let's go and meet Rocky, shall we?"

R ocky and Charlie took to each other immediately, as Jane had hoped that they would. And as they played, for the ➤

first time she heard her grandson laugh.

A few months after he'd moved in, Charlie was a different child, thanks in part to Rocky. He was now a normal soon-to-be four year old – most of the time anyway. Jane still heard him crying for his mother sometimes in the night.

It was the last day of term. Charlie had come home from nursery laden down with hand-made Christmas cards. There was one for her, one for Rocky – and one for his mother. Jane swallowed hard when she saw it.

"She can see it when she comes," Charlie said, then added anxiously, "She will come, won't she? I asked Father Christmas and he said had I been a good boy? Have I been a good boy, Granny?"

"The best." Jane's voice shook as she hugged him. "But sweetheart, she might not be able to come this Christmas."

"Father Christmas said she might…" His voice trailed away and he had that lost, empty look back in his eyes. "But I don't expect she will, will she?"

"I'm sure wherever she is, she's thinking of you," Jane murmured, wondering if now would be the right time to give him the Christmas card she'd bought for him, pretending it was from Anna.

But she hesitated. It would be a lie, wouldn't it? And it would raise his expectations, only to have them dashed.

And yet – and yet – she'd do anything to banish that bleak look in his eyes. Anything to put the smile back on his sad little face.

Just then, Rocky barked as the postman put another stack of cards through the letterbox. Charlie ran out to pick them up.

"There's one for me, Granny," he said excitedly. "Look, it's got my name on the envelope. See?"

He tore open the envelope and handed it to Jane whose hands shook as she recognised the handwriting.

Dear Charlie, she read, *I hope you have a happy Christmas with Granny. I love you to the moon and back and hope to see you soon. Lots of love, Mummy.*

And there, under the line of kisses, was a phone number. 🅜🆆

••

THE FIRST BOOK I READ…

The first book I remember reading to myself which I really loved was *The Discontented Pony* by Noel Barr. I was thrilled to find a copy at an antiques fair (!) recently. It now takes pride of place on my bookshelves.

Brain Boosters SOLUTIONS

CODEWORD FROM PAGE 27

PHRASE: GIRTON COLLEGE, CAMBRIDGE UNIVERSITY

KRISS KROSS FROM PAGE 57

MISSING LINK FROM PAGE 83

ACROSS: 2 Torch 7 Tune 8 Root
9 Dog 10 Charge 11 Heater 13 Fairy
14 Anthem 16 Growth 18 Brain
21 Typist 23 Accent 25 Gin 26 Rash
27 Rate 28 Nosed
DOWN: 1 Hush 2 Terror 3 Rider
4 Highway 5 Breast 6 Bone
12 Roman 13 Fight 15 Shotgun
17 Weight 19 Record 20 Hands
22 Year 24 Note
SHADED WORD: COSMOS

MISSING LINK FROM PAGE 137

ACROSS: 1 Bath 3 Specific 8 Eater
9 Chess 11 Chest 12 Steeple
14 Eyes 16 Nine 20 Thunder 22 Pitch
24 Puppy 26 Guide 27 Apparent
28 Legs
DOWN: 1 Branch 2 Theme 4 Phrase
5 Cycle 6 Fee 7 States 10 Seed
13 Pan 15 You 16 Napkin 17 Stop
18 Dragon 19 Chorus 21 Dryer
23 There 25 Pep
SHADED WORD: FRESCO

SUDOKU 1 FROM PAGE 155

3	2	4	6	1	9	7	5	8
9	5	8	7	2	3	6	4	1
6	7	1	8	4	5	9	2	3
7	4	3	5	8	1	2	9	6
2	6	9	4	3	7	1	8	5
8	1	5	9	6	2	3	7	4
4	8	2	1	9	6	5	3	7
5	3	6	2	7	8	4	1	9
1	9	7	3	5	4	8	6	2

SUDOKU 2 FROM PAGE 155

1	2	7	8	5	6	4	9	3
6	8	3	4	9	2	1	5	7
4	9	5	1	7	3	2	8	6
8	4	6	9	3	5	7	1	2
7	5	1	6	2	4	8	3	9
9	3	2	7	8	1	5	6	4
5	6	9	2	4	8	3	7	1
2	7	8	3	1	9	6	4	5
3	1	4	5	6	7	9	2	8

WORD WHEEL FROM PAGE 155 The nine-letter word is PARTRIDGE

With Love From Mum

This Christmas could never be the same – but maybe it could be touched with a different kind of magic

By Carole Llewellyn

The doorbell rang. Lisa made her way down the hall expecting to see Mark and the children home early. She'd thought it too good to be true when he'd suggested taking them to the park.

"It'll give you chance to wrap the presents without worrying about their inquisitive eyes," he'd said.

These days she never seemed to have much time to herself. It was almost as if Mark was afraid to leave her on her own – and who could blame him?

Lisa opened the front door.

"Hello, Lisa darling."

"Mum?" Lisa whispered. "Mum – is it really you?"

"And who else would it be?" her mother scoffed, softly touching Lisa's face as she entered the hallway and made her way to the living room.

As she passed, the spicy smell of her mother's favourite lavender cologne filled the air. Taking a deep breath, Lisa, as if in a trance, followed the fragrance.

"I must say the room looks very festive, dear. You can't beat a real Christmas tree. Keep your imitation, that's what I say." Her mother settled herself into the large easy chair by the fireplace.

In previous years decorating the house

and wrapping presents had been a joy – but this year was different. This year Lisa was simply going through the motions "for the sake of the children". The truth was it could never be the same.

"Mum? I don't understand."

"I was on my way to the church carol service, and I thought I'd call in to help you wrap the presents. I saw Mark leave with the children. They're all looking well – a real credit to you."

Lisa pinched herself hard and winced as the sharp pain told her she must be awake. Maybe she'd finally cracked.

Doctor Baxter had said she was heading for a nervous breakdown if she didn't pull herself together.

Lisa slumped into the chair opposite her mother.

"Mum – are you all right?" she heard herself ask, shaking her head at such a daft question.

"I'm fine, dear. Why wouldn't I be? Alice Logan and I are having a whale of a time. You remember Alice? She used to live next door to us. We went to school together, you know? It was so nice to see her again. By the way, I called in on ➟

your father this morning, but he was fast asleep. I didn't want to wake him. Never mind, I'll call next time."

For what seemed like an age Lisa sat in silence watching her mother expertly wrap the presents as she had so many times in the past, scared that the least sound might break whatever magic spell had given her this time with her mother.

Then, in the distance, Lisa heard the wall clock chime once, twice, three and four times.

"Goodness, is that the time?" Her mother stood up and walked towards Lisa. "I really must go now."

As her mother came closer, Lisa reached out and touched her hand. It felt soft and warm and… *normal?*

"Take care of yourself, my dear. You're looking a bit peaky. Give the children a big hug for me, and my love to Mark. You've got a good one there, love."

Lisa tried to get out of the chair to follow her, but her legs wouldn't move.

"Goodbye, Mum," she whispered. Then, raising her hands to her face, she finally gave way to tears – tears she'd been holding back for months.

Hello – we're home!" Lisa opened her eyes to see Mark and the children. She smiled, knowing something had changed. A warm glow engulfed her, and for the first time in months she felt at peace.

"Lisa, is everything all right? It's not like you to doze off in the chair – especially with the front door wide open!"

"Oh, Mark. You're not going to believe what happened. My mother's been here! I actually saw her, she –"

"Sophie, take Justin to play in your bedroom, there's a good girl. I'll call you when tea's ready – OK, love."

Mark spoke very calmly but Lisa could tell, by the look in his eyes that he was upset with her.

"Can we have pizza? I love pizza," Sophie asked.

"Me too," Justin added, determined not to be left out.

"We'll see – now, off you go." Lisa watched as Mark gently ushered them out of the room.

"Mark, I know what you're thinking. But I swear, Mum was definitely here! She sat in the chair and wrapped all the children's presents – look!"

She pointed to the neatly wrapped

pile under the tree, smiling at him. He turned away in frustration.

"Why can't you accept that your mother's dead? She died three months ago! You're making yourself ill. You're not eating, you're not sleeping and now this. I tell you, I'm at my wits' end."

"Mark, I know how worried you are and I've tried so hard to pull myself together. I know I'm not the first person to have lost someone close, but I didn't have time to say goodbye. Until today, I'd felt so… cheated."

Mark frowned. "Why don't you go upstairs and lie down for a while? I'm going to call Doctor Baxter."

Lisa did as she was told. She couldn't be angry with Mark. After all, why should he believe her? She was having difficulty believing it herself.

When the doctor phoned back, he explained to Lisa that her "vision" was normal. "Grief affects people in different ways. You wanted to see your mother so badly you allowed your mind to play tricks on you. It's nothing a good night sleep won't put right, I'm sure. I'll prescribe a mild sedative for Mark to pick up."

Lisa turned her head away. Why wouldn't anyone believe her?

"Mummy, Daddy, come and see what Father Christmas brought me!" Sophie shrieked with excitement.

"And me," Justin added, with a mouthful of chocolate buttons.

It was such a joy to see their happy, smiling faces.

After opening their presents the children were too excited and too full of chocolate to want anything to eat. Mark and Lisa enjoyed a leisurely breakfast and exchanged gifts.

She'd almost finished tidying and saw a small, unopened present under the tree

A Merry Christmas, my darling." Mark said, bending down to kiss her lips. "The children are downstairs opening their presents – shall we join them?"

"A Merry Christmas to you too. And, Mark, thank you for being so understanding. I know these past few months haven't been easy," she said, returning a long lingering kiss.

Lisa meant every word. Since his outburst after her mother's "visit" Mark had never again reproached her, even though he must have thought she'd completely lost it.

In fact, the opposite had happened. Since seeing her mother, she seemed to have come to terms with her loss; there had been no more sleepless nights, her appetite had returned and, for a while now, she had been able to remember her mother fondly without falling apart.

"Last one downstairs makes the breakfast," she called as she jumped out of bed and grabbed her dressing gown.

"That's not fair!" Mark laughed, trying to overtake her on the stairs.

She felt good. With the tension of recent months gone, it was more like the happiness of old times.

"OK, kids. It's time to pick up Grandpa. Let's leave Mummy some peace and quiet for a while. We'll be back within the hour, love," Mark said, giving her a big hug.

As soon as they'd gone Lisa began clearing up the Christmas wrapping paper so urgently discarded by the children in their haste to get at their presents.

She'd almost finished when she saw a small, unopened parcel under the tree. She picked it up and began to slowly unwrap it. Inside, she found a red velvet box containing her mother's treasured string of pearls – and a small note.

Dear Lisa, my beloved daughter.
A very Merry Christmas and…
a fond goodbye!
Love, Mum. 🆆

THE AUTHOR SAYS…

This story was inspired by my own personal experience. I was 17 when I lost my mother and, not long afterwards, I could have sworn I caught sight of her walking down the high street. As I say in the story; grief affects people in different ways. And the mind can and will play tricks on you.

A Precious Gift

Hope was feeling jaded and despondent – until her wise old Grandpa Nick gave her the greatest gift of all…

By H. Johnson-Mack

It seemed apt that just when Hope arrived at her grandfather's cottage, a few flakes of snow should start to fall. She had always connected Christmas with Grandpa Nick, not only because of his name but also his lovely, lush beard.

Now it was even more like the fabled Saint Nicholas, she noticed as she wandered round to the back garden in response to his call. It was the perfect shade of snowy white with a pair of twinkling eyes above it.

She had no chance to remark upon this, though, for he had a finger to his lips and was pointing to the ground beyond his spade. Hope smiled at the jaunty little

make such an effort with it and," he patted her hand, "nothing compares to face-to-face contact. Besides, you know what they say about all work and no play…"

"I'm fine, Grandpa."

"Really?" He looked doubtful. "You don't look your normal chirpy self to me."

Hope shrugged.

"I'm just a bit tired, that's all. The flat took ages to sell after Simon and I broke up. And there's a lot more to setting up a business than I realised, even an online one. I haven't even had time to put up my decorations yet. Unlike you…" she added at sight of the sparkling Christmas tree in the lounge window.

Nick grinned as he eased off his Wellingtons.

Their break-up had left Hope with a bitterness toward this time of year

robin sitting there looking up at them.

"Ah…" Grandpa Nick sighed as with one final wink, the robin flew away. "The gardener's companion. Like something off a Christmas card, wasn't he?" He gave Hope a hearty hug, tucking her arm beneath his as they turned to go inside. "It's lovely to see you, girl."

"I'm sorry it's been so long," Hope said guiltily. "I've been busy, what with the business and everything. But there's always Skype if you wanted to see me."

Nick waved that suggestion aside.

"I don't hold with this new-fangled technology, love. People don't have to

"It's good this year, isn't it? A new artificial Norway spruce. So, no time to put up a tree, eh? I bet you haven't been to a carol service yet, either."

"Not yet."

"Huh! And this from the girl who always used to adore Christmas!"

Hope pushed aside her memories of last December, when she and her childhood sweetheart finally admitted they'd outgrown each other. No more than old habit they might have been, but it was still hard to say goodbye, and it had left Hope with a bitterness toward this time of year she now tried to shrug off.

"All that festive stuff is for kids."

"Rubbish!" Nick declared. "Don't you remember your Christmas carols, girl? Yet in thy dark streets shineth the everlasting light… Oh come all ye faithful. How are such sentiments just for children?"

Hope had been looking over his work table, where a handful of clock faces lay in various states of repair. Strange that a house covered in timepieces could be so reassuringly ageless.

"You look pretty busy yourself, Grandpa," she said. "I thought you'd retired from horology."

Nick came to join her, running his fingers lovingly over the nearest, a square face with Art Deco-style digits.

"When your job is also your hobby, you never really retire. And I just can't resist tinkering with these poor timepieces, crafted so carefully and for now, fallen silent. Like this one…"

He lifted an ivory-and-gold pocket watch into his palm.

"It belonged to my grandad, your great-grandfather, travelled with him to the trenches and home again. Isn't that marvellous? A little piece of ticking history that fits in your pocket." He frowned as he added, "It's so very easy to take for →

granted, is time. Remember that."

Laying the watch back down, he smiled brightly at Hope.

"Now, tell me, what can I get my favourite girl for Christmas? I seem so out of touch with you these days."

Hope laughed.

"Oh, nothing too much, Grandpa. Just get me socks or something."

"I'd never dream of buying you anything so unimaginative!" Nick snorted, the twinkle reappearing in his eye when he caught sight of Hope's expression.

"Well, that's me back to the shops, then," she mumbled.

He laughed.

"Well, before you do, come and have a cuppa with your old grandpa. If you're not too busy, that is."

Hope followed him into the kitchen, taking the kettle from his hand with a rueful smile.

"I think I can manage that."

Oh holy night! The stars are brightly shining…

Hope sighed and laying her head against Grandpa Nick's arm, let her eyes wander…

St Bartholomew's church was swathed in seasonal greenery, candlelight softly flickering as the choir began to sing one of her favourite carols.

He was right, she reflected. It was all too easy to allow the responsibilities of adulthood to eclipse everything else. But there was so much more to life, so many things to enjoy. Like this, for instance. Just giving up that little bit of time to go with your grandfather to church and you could be a child again, basking in the warmth and wonder of this special season.

"Is everything OK?" Nick whispered.

The choir's symphonic voices soared up to the rafters. *Oh, hear the angel voices. Oh, night divine!*

"Oh, yes," Hope breathed back, smiling. "In fact, it's perfect."

By the time Christmas morning arrived, the prospect of its being white had long since faded. But the glimmer of sunshine was just as welcome for Hope's family tradition of a walk to build up an appetite for the big lunch.

Before that, there was just time to open a few presents waiting patiently beneath the tree.

Hope couldn't hide a smile when Grandpa Nick opened her gift; a new watchmaker's toolkit tucked cheekily beneath a pair of socks.

"I hope you like mine," he said, handing over a small package.

"You've already given me something," Hope reminded him. "You gave me back my love of Christmas."

Then she gasped, staring down at her ancestor's watch.

"Oh, Grandpa! It's beautiful!"

"And the best present I could ever give you," said Nick. "The gift of time."

"Ah, yes," Hope agreed, smiling. "A piece of ticking history that fits neatly in your pocket…" Ⓜ

• •

THE FIRST BOOK I READ...

I read loads growing up but some of the earliest I remember were Enid Blyton's *Magic Faraway Tree* books. How I longed to find that enchanted wood and zoom down the Slippery-Slip!

Each Week For You To Enjoy

My Weekly

Amazing Cookery

Favourite Celebrities

Up-to-date Health News

Fabulous Fiction

Your Feel Good Read

PLUS

◆ **Puzzles** ◆ **Fashion** ◆ **Beauty** ◆ **Real Life**

You'll Love It!
On Sale Every Tuesday